the
binding force

the binding force

by Scientists of the Westinghouse
Research Laboratories

DANIEL BERG
ROBERT CHARLES
LAWRENCE EPSTEIN
MILTON GOTTLIEB
LYON MANDELCORN
JAMES McHUGH
ARMAND PANSON
SHARON BANIGAN, *Executive Editor*

A Westinghouse Search Book

WALKER AND COMPANY
NEW YORK

Other Westinghouse Search Books

THE SCIENCE OF SCIENCE
ENERGY DOES MATTER
ELECTRONS ON THE MOVE
SCIENCE BY DEGREES
MATH AND AFTERMATH
CRYSTALS: PERFECT AND IMPERFECT
SEVEN STATES OF MATTER

Contents

APPENDIX

Foreword

DURING THE LAST century the number of scientists in the world has approximately doubled every twelve years. The number of scientific discoveries may not have increased quite in proportion; but there is no doubt that the body of knowledge that we call science has also increased very rapidly.

Fifty years ago, when I began the serious study of chemistry, the subject consisted largely of disconnected facts. The number of chemical facts now known is far greater, but it is, I believe, now much easier to achieve a mastery of science than it was then.

As chemistry has grown and developed during the past fifty years, it has also become simpler, because of the discovery of theoretical principles that constitute a framework to which the facts of chemistry can be attached in an orderly way.

One of the most valuable theories of chemistry is the theory of the chemical bond. Every student of chemistry can benefit by obtaining, as early in his course of study as possible, an understanding of the chemical bond.

In this book, *The Binding Force,* the authors have presented a simple and straightforward discussion of the chemical bond and the structure of molecules. I am sure that the book will be of value to many young people just embarking on their own voyages of discovery of the world.

LINUS PAULING

Preface

THE APPROACH in this book is a conceptual one. We hope that what will result clearly is the concept of the chemical bond in its various aspects. We have chosen a non-rigorous presentation; we are not attempting to derive theorems from first principles, but, hopefully, we will succeed in showing that an understanding of bonds and matter does obtain from first principles. Our intention, too, is to re-create the atmosphere of excitement that is inherent in modern chemistry as an evolving, incomplete, experimental and theoretical science, since we feel that only in such an atmosphere can the reader find intellectual stimulation, and fully appreciate the vitality of the ideas that will be discussed.

THE AUTHORS
Pittsburgh, Pennsylvania

PART
1

Bonds
in General

Perspective

A WORLD WITHOUT BONDS? Possible perhaps, but it takes a vivid imagination to grasp all the implications of such a situation. The chemical bond is so all-pervading a concept in an environment seemingly dominated by physical phenomena that it is indeed difficult to visualize our world without such bonds. The properties of matter are determined, for the most part, by the character of the chemical bonds that constitute the matter. For example, the concept of hydrogen coupling the oxygens of two water molecules, which will be discussed in detail in Chapters Four and Six, is of prime importance to the comparatively high melting and boiling points of water—a molecule with a molecular weight of only 18. Because of this property, life as we know it here on earth is possible. Also, the phosphate bond, linking phosphorus and oxygen, has evolved as the main energy transferring mechanism in life systems. The reason for this evolution can be derived from the peculiarities of the phosphorus-oxygen bond itself. The transport of oxygen in the body is based on the bond between oxygen and hemoglobin, a bond that can be reversibly formed or broken as the occasion demands.

To take a more plebeian view of the importance of bonds, we can consider that most of our energy utilization is based on the oxidation of some kind of fuel, forming, in general, carbon-oxygen and hydrogen-oxygen bonds. We would certainly agree with anyone who claimed that this view may be somewhat behind the times, since the major production of energy in the future will undoubtedly be either nuclear fission or nuclear fusion, and perhaps both. However, the materials that will enable such an energy source to become commonplace are based on the peculiarities of the bonds between atoms, giving materials their specific properties.

Precisely what *is* a bond? To answer this question, we might paraphrase Linus Pauling: a bond exists between two or more atoms when the forces between the atoms are sufficient to make an aggregate with enough stability so that it is convenient to consider the aggregate as an independent molecular species. Or, more simply stated, a bond ties two atoms together to form a molecular entity with sufficient stability for us to measure or describe some of its properties.

There are many kinds of bonds that can be described, such as the *ionic bond,* the *covalent bond,* the *hydrogen bond,* and so on. But the feature common to all bonds is that they are essentially electronic in nature. The electrons that surround the nucleus determine the fundamental character of an atom, as well as the fundamental character of a molecule. A description of the bond in a molecule is intimately involved with the electronic distribution in the molecule.

There are a number of questions we hope to answer in the discussions that follow: Why do atoms form bonds with each other? Why do specific numbers of atoms in definite proportions bond together in a single molecule? How can we measure the structure of molecules in order to describe the bonds between atoms in the molecules? What is the nature of a bond as it is being formed or broken? Then, too, we will describe many interesting bonds found in unusual compounds, as well as those in life processes.

THE PERSPECTIVE OF HISTORY

Today our picture of molecules and their bonding is derived from the contributions of many people. As early as 1807, John Dalton made his hypothesis of the atom as an indivisible entity, which may sound trite today but was an enormous forward stride at the time. Then about 1819, Gay-Lussac and Berzelius formulated the law of multiple proportions, which states that atoms combine in definite ratios to form molecules. A little more than three decades were to pass before Frankland, in 1852, and then Kekulé in 1858, described a theory of valence which claimed that an atom was like a ball having a fixed number of hooks and that this arrangement determined the number of other atoms, which also had hooks, that could be attached directly to it. It was Kekulé who also introduced the method of depicting structures by drawing lines between atoms to indicate bonds, a method still used today. Another important contribution was made in 1861, when Butlerov used the term "chemical structure," and stated that the structure of a chemical compound determined its properties. In 1869, Mendeleev made a contribution of the utmost importance—his periodic chart of the elements. Here the elements were arranged in a repeating array, in which the properties of atoms formed families. This momentous generalization acquired additional significance when the Bohr atomic theory explained the periodicity, which will be described in more detail in Chapter Two. The brilliant postulate that the carbon atom tended to form tetrahedral bonds was made by Van't Hoff and Le Bel in 1874, and it was this hypothesis that later made it possible to describe the stereochemical properties of many carbon compounds. Up to the present century, all of the hypotheses mentioned above remained simply that. It was not until the discovery of the electron in 1897 that a description of the chemical bond could be made which would include all of these hypotheses as derived conclusions.

A paper published in 1916 by G. N. Lewis probably forms the basis of the modern atomic theory of valence. In this paper, Lewis not only discussed empirically the formation of ions by a completion of stable shells of electrons, but he also described the formation of a chemical bond by the sharing of two electrons between atoms. Irving Langmuir expanded these ideas and showed that many of the known facts of chemistry could be clarified by Lewis' concept. These ideas serve to show the relationship of the periodic table and the *valence*, or number of bonds, that atoms tend to utilize. The difficulty with the Lewis theory was that it assumed that the electrons were at rest and not in dynamic equilibrium. If, indeed, they were at static equilibrium, then the forces between atoms would necessarily be of the coulombic type, and these forces are not sufficient to describe the bonds in such molecules as hydrogen. An improvement in the situation came about with the amplification of Niels Bohr's efforts, which he had started in 1913. Essentially, his theory stated that each electron in an atom moved in a fixed orbit. Bohr's theory will be discussed in somewhat greater detail in Chapter Two, but it will suffice here to say that the theory proved inadequate when it came to bonds containing several electrons. However, Bohr's theory represented a tremendous advance, because of its dynamic character and because it introduced quantum mechanics to explain bonding. The more recent theory, now called *wave mechanics,* was first proposed by Erwin Schrödinger in 1926, and it was able to give a more detailed account of the motions of electrons, both in atoms and in molecules. This theory allowed an understanding of Lewis' empirical, but profound, insight of shared electrons in bonds to be derived from first principles. On the basis of wave mechanics, a fairly coherent and inclusive theory of molecular structure has been developed. More recent workers, including Pauling, Feynman, and Mulliken, to name only a few, have utilized quantum theory to extend and elaborate the theory of chemical bonding. This is a continuing process, and people are adding both to the theory and to the data on which the theory is based, as well as to the pictorial, conceptual approach of a qualitative nature.

A comprehensive view of the modern theory of the chemical bond is given in Chapters Two and Three. This covers such bonds as the ionic bond, covalent shared electron bond, bonds in metal, and the Van der Waals bond. It should be re-emphasized, however, that all of these bonds are electronic in nature. The chapters that follow will utilize these theories to describe some modern work in bonds.

THE UBIQUITOUS CHEMICAL BOND

Whenever we want to get to the root of why certain materials have the basic characteristics they do, such as hardness, melting point, electrical properties, and so on, the major prerequisite is an understanding of the nature of bonds. The reason for this is that basically the properties of matter derive from the nature of the bonds that make

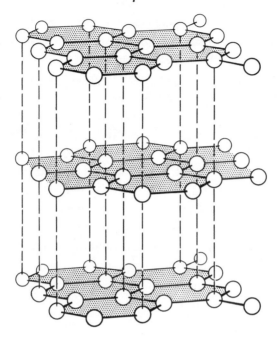

Figure 1.1. The structure of graphite.

up the matter. For example, graphite consists of layers of carbon atoms which are packed in hexagonal rings, much like the hexagonal tile found in some old-fashioned bathrooms built when porcelain was still used. These hexagonal blocks fit together to make a layer. The hexagons are formed by carbon atoms located at each of the six points of the hexagon; one carbon atom is bonded to three other carbon atoms within the three hexagons that share an edge, as shown in Fig. 1.1. (Actually, each bond is the equivalent of about $1\frac{1}{3}$ carbon-carbon bonds, as in ethane, H_3C-CH_3. See Chapters Two and Three.) The reason that graphite is a good lubricant is that these planes of hexagonally arranged carbon atoms are fairly readily sheared, and can slip one over another. It has been found recently, however, that either water vapor or oxygen are needed for the planes to separate easily and slide over each other. But it is the basic layer structure of graphite that allows it to be a lubricant. Now, diamond also consists of pure carbon atoms. But here the carbon atoms are arranged tetrahedrally with respect to each other. This means that diamond has a three-dimensional structure with each carbon atom bonded to four other carbon atoms which do not lie in the same plane, as shown in Fig. 1.2. This type of bonding allows the carbon atoms to be very strongly held to each other in a giant three-dimensional molecule. We might say that each individual crystal is a single molecule of carbon. Because the bonding is of this form, diamond is extremely hard and quite different from the very soft graphitic form, although in both cases the only constituent is simply carbon.

To emphasize the role of bonds in determining the property of a material, we can see that because the four bonds from the carbon atoms are in a tetrahedral arrangement, diamond is electrically insulating, colorless, and one of the hardest substances known, so hard, in fact, that it is used industrially as an abrasive. Graphite, on the other hand, is electrically conducting, black, and useful as a solid lubricant, simply because its bonding is shared in a repeated manner with its three adjacent atoms of carbon. Its electrical conductivity and lubricity make graphite suitable for commutating brushes in electrical machines. That these two forms of the same element can have such vastly different properties is a direct result of the chemical bonding.

Water, and the hydrogen bonding associated with it, is another example with much more profound implications. Imagine a world where water boiled at approximately $-150°C$! This would happen if the water molecules did not associate with one another to form a liquid

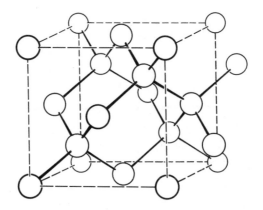

Figure 1.2. The structure of diamond.

consisting of clumps of water molecules, rather than dissociated, individual molecules. Let's compare it with methane (CH_4), which has about the same volume and molecular weight as water. Water freezes at $0°C$ and boils at $100°C$, whereas liquid methane freezes at $-184°C$ and boils at $-161°C$. Although water and methane differ in molecular weight by only two units, the difference in their boiling points is $260°C$. The hydrogen bond between water molecules explains the difference. Another consequence of this interesting type of bond is that water freezes to an open-structure ice phase, which is of a lower density than the liquid phase—a distinct deviation from the behavior of most materials. This allows the formation of ice on the surface rather than the bottom of natural bodies of water during the winter. The ice layer serves to protect aquatic life and has a profound influence on climatic conditions. We have seen that the properties of water are distinctly dependent on the joining together of the molecules. The concept of the hydrogen bond is also of the utmost importance in understanding the structure of protein, which is the basic constituent of all life. (See Chapter Seven.) It is the hydrogen bond that gives the structure to the nucleic acid molecule, and it is this structure of the nucleic acid molecule that enables living systems to reproduce and grow.

Throughout the rest of the book, many more examples will dramatize the profound differences that result from slight and subtle changes in the bonds between atoms.

The basic concept of the bond is introduced in Chapter Two with a description of atomic structure and some simple bonds. Chapter Three first re-emphasizes a few essential points that have been discussed, and then goes on to describe bonds in condensed states, such as bonds in crystals, in metals, and in semiconductors. Such questions as why metals conduct electricity are also answered. At this point, the basic tools are on hand for understanding the discussions that follow. Chapter Four views the chemical bond as it is being formed and broken. Some of the recent work in bonds, which is not only fundamental but of particular interest, is presented in Chapters Five and Six. The discussions include the bonds in noble gas compounds, erroneously referred to until recently as the inert gases. Coordination complexes, which involve a type of bond that is of unusual importance in life, are introduced in Chapter Four, and later described from a different point of view in Chapter Seven. In Chapter Five, Van der Waals bonds are reviewed; these are the *unspecific* bonds between molecules and atoms, that is, bonds that occur between every molecule and every atom, even molecules and atoms of the same species! This chapter also includes a description of clathrates. Chapter Seven is devoted to the fascinating subject of bonds in life, and here the most recent information about bonds in proteins and nucleic acid is presented. The final chapter gives illustrations of some of the modern techniques used for identifying and describing the chemical bond, including optical spectroscopy, nuclear magnetic resonance, electron spin resonance, Mössbauer absorption, and x-ray and neutron diffraction.

Whether the discussion concerns the secret of life itself, or drugs, polymers, semiconductors, or structural materials, it will become apparent that the all-pervading basic entity is the nature of the chemical bond, the binding forces that hold all matter together.

2

Directed Bonds

BEFORE WE CAN discuss bonds, we must consider the structure and the properties of atoms that make bonds possible. An atom consists of a positively charged nucleus, surrounded by negatively charged electrons. The hydrogen atom is the simplest; its nucleus is composed of a single proton, "surrounded" by one electron. The mass of the electron is only 1/1837 the mass of the hydrogen atom, so that nearly all of the atomic mass is concentrated in the nucleus. This is true not only of the hydrogen atom but of all other atoms as well. The nuclei of heavier atoms contain uncharged neutrons, as well as protons. The number of protons in the nucleus is equal to the atomic number of the element, each proton contributing one unit of positive charge. (One unit of charge is the amount of charge carried by one electron—1.6×10^{-19} coulombs—and the sign is positive or negative, depending on whether the particle is a proton or an electron.) The number of neutrons is similar to the number of protons, being roughly equal in the case of the light elements, and somewhat greater in the heavy elements. The sum of the masses of the protons and neutrons in the nucleus is very nearly equal to the atomic weight of the element. In the neutral atom, the number of surrounding electrons is equal to the number of protons in the nucleus.

Since the nucleus plays only a minor role in any discussion of bonding, our interest is almost exclusively in the surrounding electrons. In some cases, however, the mass of the nucleus is of some importance, particularly in the case of very light elements. For example, hydrogen and deuterium have the same chemical behavior in general, but the presence of the neutron in the nucleus of deuterium effectively doubles the mass of the atom in comparison to hydrogen, so that such properties as molecular vibration frequencies are changed when deuterium is substituted for hydrogen in a molecule. Such isotopic substitution is of great practical use in a number of spectroscopic techniques for the determination of molecular structures.

ELECTRONS

Let's now look at the electron per se, and then see how it behaves in the atomic environment. For most purposes, the electron can conveniently be regarded as a particle. However, a beam of electrons produces diffraction phenomena analogous to those observed with light; to explain these, a wave theory is required, according to which a beam of light consists of a train of waves. On the other hand, many facts connected with electromagnetic radiation can be explained only by considering light to consist of discrete energy packets, called *photons*, which travel at a rate of 3×10^{10} centimeters per second (the speed of light). The quantum theory of radiation, developed by Max Planck and by Albert Einstein, related the energy of a photon to the frequency of the radiation with the equation

$$E = h\nu, \qquad (2.1)$$

where ν is the frequency and h is a universal constant, called *Planck's constant*, equal to 6.6×10^{-27} erg sec. Thus, electromagnetic radiation has a dual nature, whereby gross effects, such as diffraction and interference phenomena, are most easily understood in terms of wave theory, and effects involving mechanisms on the atomic scale, such as the photoelectric effect, require the quantum theory.

In 1924, the French physicist Louis-Victor de Broglie first suggested a similar dual nature for material particles and electrons, and derived the relationship

$$\lambda = \frac{h}{mv}, \tag{2.2}$$

which relates the wavelength λ to the momentum of a particle mv by way of Planck's constant h. Eq. 2.2 is of fundamental importance and led to the development of quantum or wave mechanics.

Now let's consider some properties of electrons in atoms. When an atom is excited—by heating to a high temperature, for example—it emits light. The light, when passed through a spectrograph, is found to consist of a series of discrete wavelengths or lines. If the excited atoms are in a strong magnetic field, many of the lines are "split" into two or more lines. These spectral patterns are specific for a given element; that is, the lines always occur at precisely the same wavelengths or frequencies for a given element, and every element has a different pattern or spectrum. Some spectra are extremely complex, containing many hundreds of lines. Any theory of atomic structure must be able to explain such atomic spectra; indeed, the painstaking work of a great many spectroscopists has contributed immeasurably to our understanding of the structure of atoms.

In a classic experiment in 1911, the British physicist Ernest Rutherford showed that the atom consisted of a heavy positively charged nucleus, surrounded at some distance by the electrons. To account for the fact that the electrons did not fall into the nucleus as a result of electrostatic attraction, he postulated that the electrons rotated rapidly about the nucleus, so that the attractive force inward was exactly balanced by the outward centrifugal force. However, this "planetary" analogy is contrary to the laws of classical electromagnetic theory, which require that a charged particle accelerating in an electric field emit radiation during its motion. (Remember that a particle moving with speed v in a circle of radius r has an acceleration v^2/r toward the center.) Thus, according to the classical theory, the electron would be radiating energy continuously, so that the radius of curvature of its path would steadily decrease, the electron eventually spiraling into the nucleus. There is also the difficulty of explaining the emission of definite spectral lines, which, according to quantum theory, should correspond to definite amounts of energy, instead of a continuous spectrum covering all frequencies.

In order to circumvent these difficulties, Niels Bohr suggested in 1913 that an electron always moved in a closed orbit and, as long as it remained in this orbit, it did not absorb or emit radiation. In effect, Bohr was saying that, since classical theory could not explain the then-known properties of atoms, the atom must be outside the realm of classical theory. This was bold and imaginative thinking on his part. Furthermore, according to Bohr, any electron could reside in more than one stable orbit, each orbit being called a *stationary state,* or in modern terminology, an *energy level.* According to Bohr's theory, the number of such energy levels is determined by the quantum condition that the angular momentum of an electron is an integral multiple of $h/2\pi$, where h is Planck's constant. At this time, there appeared to be no reason for the quantization of momentum in $h/2\pi$ units except that it worked; it was not until the development of wave mechanics, over a decade later, that this hypothesis was theoretically justified. The angular momentum of a particle, moving in a circular orbit, is mvr, so according to the Bohr theory, possible orbits satisfy the relationship

$$mvr = n\frac{h}{2\pi}, \tag{2.3}$$

where n is an integer called the *quantum number* of the particular energy level. Finally, Bohr postulated that when an electron jumps from one energy level to another, radiation of a definite frequency is emitted or absorbed. The frequency v of the radiation depends on the energy of the initial and final states of the electron, according to the relationship

$$E_1 - E_2 = hv. \tag{2.4}$$

The Bohr theory provides a convenient picture of the atom, and it is able to account quantitatively for the spectrum of the hydrogen atom. However, it suffers some important weaknesses. For example, it yields incorrect results for the spectra of more complex atoms. Another difficulty is that the concept of planetary electron orbits implies, for hydrogen at least, a flat atom, which is contrary to the results of experiment. Still another difficulty—although it was not brought out until the development of quantum mechanics—is that the exact definition of position (or orbit) *and* momentum is contrary to the *uncertainty principle,* which is regarded as a basic law of physics.

The uncertainty principle, put forth by W. Heisenberg in 1927, states that the simultaneous determination of position and momentum is impossible. It requires that if Δx is the uncertainty in determining the position of any electron and Δp is the uncertainty in determining the momentum, then the uncertainty of the product $\Delta x \Delta p$ is on the order of Planck's constant, h.

In 1926, Erwin Schrödinger utilized the de Broglie relation (Eq. 2.2) to derive an equation that bears his name, relating the behavior of an electron to its energy and the potential field in which it moves. The solutions to this equation are called *wave functions,* and are usually given the symbol Ψ. The physical significance of the wave function is that its square is proportional to the *probability* of finding an electron in some particular volume in space at any time. Thus, in the quantum mechanical description of an atom, the specific orbits of Bohr are replaced by probabilities. A useful physical analogy is to think of the electron as a smeared-out region of charge, or a "charge cloud," the density of this cloud at any point being proportional to the square of the electron's wave function at that point.

QUANTUM NUMBERS AND ATOMS

The results of experimental spectroscopy and other experimental techniques, combined with the results of quantum mechanics, allow us to build up a fairly detailed picture of the structure of the atom. Each electron in an atom can be described by a set of four quantum numbers. These quantum numbers are a series of constants which arise in the solutions of the Schrödinger equation. They have a direct correspondence to quantities developed in the analysis of line spectra, and the spectroscopic notation is still commonly used. These quantum numbers, together with their equivalents in spectroscopic notation, are:

n = principal quantum number, which indicates the energy "shell" occupied by the electron. In spectroscopic notation, the K, L, M, N, . . . shells correspond to $n = 1, 2, 3, 4, . . .$, respectively.

l = azimuthal quantum number, which is a measure of the angular momentum of the electron. It can have values of 0, 1, 2, ... $(n - 1)$, corresponding to s, p, d, f, . . . in spectroscopic notation.

m = magnetic quantum number, which describes the behavior of the electron in a magnetic field. It can have the values 0, ± 1, $\pm 2, \ldots, \pm l$.

s = spin quantum number, which describes the electron spin. It has values of $+\frac{1}{2}$ or $-\frac{1}{2}$.

The *Pauli exclusion principle* states that no two electrons in the same atom can have the same set of quantum numbers. The application of this principle enables us to build systematically the atomic structure of every atom in the periodic table. Hydrogen has only one electron, and so in its *ground state*, as the state of lowest energy is called, $n = 1$, $l = 0$, $m = 0$, and s can be either $+\frac{1}{2}$ or $-\frac{1}{2}$. Helium has two electrons, hence $n = 1$, $l = 0$, $m = 0$, and s must be $+\frac{1}{2}$ for one electron and $-\frac{1}{2}$ for the other. If we look at the allowable values for the various quantum numbers, we see we have now exhausted the possibilities of $n = 1$, so that for lithium, with three electrons, the third electron must go into the $n = 2$ level. Similarly, in the case of beryllium, with four electrons, two are in the $n = 1$ shell, and two are in the $n = 2$ shell with $l = 0$, $m = 0$, and $s = +\frac{1}{2}$ for one and $-\frac{1}{2}$ for the other. In boron, the fifth electron must go into the $n = 2$, $l = 1$ state. We can continue this process until we reach neon, with ten electrons, where we find we have exhausted all possible combinations of the four quantum numbers for $n = 2$, and the next electron (to make sodium) must go into the $n = 3$ level.

A given set of n, l, and m values can accommodate two electrons of opposite spin. Such a set of three quantum numbers describes an *orbital*. The first, or K, level of an atom has only one orbital, called the $1s$ orbital, with $l = 0$. In the second, or L, level four orbitals are available, the $2s$ orbital (with $l = 0$) and three $2p$ orbitals (with $l = 1$, $m = 1$, 0, $+1$). Similarly, when $n = 3$, we have available a total of nine orbitals, one s orbital, three p orbitals, and five d orbitals. The approximate energy level relationships for the various orbitals are shown in Fig. 2.1. We see that for a given value of n, the s orbital is of lowest energy and will therefore be the first orbital filled, followed

Figure 2.1. Relative energy levels of atomic orbitals.

by the p, and so on. However, as we get to higher values of n, the situation changes somewhat. As we see, the $4s$ level is slightly lower in energy than the $3d$, so that the $4s$ level is filled before the $3d$. Table 2.A lists the total number of electrons in each kind of orbital for neutral atoms in the ground state, for approximately the first half of the periodic table.

Two additional points must be made at this time. In general, equivalent orbitals will each be occupied by one electron, until all have one electron each before pairing occurs. For example, the ground state electronic distribution in the $2p$ orbitals in carbon will be as shown in Fig. 2.2.

Another point is that, where possible, an atom prefers to have a set

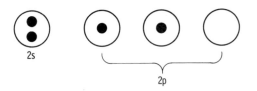

Figure 2.2. Ground state electron distribution in carbon.

TABLE 2.A

Electron Configuration of Atoms in Their Normal States

		$1s$	$2s$	$2p$	$3s$	$3p$	$3d$	$4s$	$4p$	$4d$	$5s$	$5p$
H	1	1										
He	2	2										
Li	3	2	1									
Be	4	2	2									
B	5	2	2	1								
C	6	2	2	2								
N	7	2	2	3								
O	8	2	2	4								
F	9	2	2	5								
Ne	10	2	2	6								
Na	11				1							
Mg	12				2							
Al	13		10		2	1						
Si	14		Neon core		2	2						
P	15				2	3						
S	16				2	4						
Cl	17				2	5						
Ar	18	2	2	6	2	6						
K	19							1				
Ca	20							2				
Sc	21						1	2				
Ti	22						2	2				
V	23						3	2				
Cr	24						5	1				
Ma	25						5	2				
Fe	26			18			6	2				
Co	27			Argon core			7	2				
Ni	28						8	2				
Cu	29						10	1				
Zn	30						10	2				
Ga	31						10	2	1			
Ge	32						10	2	2			
As	33						10	2	3			
Se	34						10	2	4			
Br	35						10	2	5			
Kr	36	2	2	6	2	6	10	2	6			
Rb	37										1	
Sr	38										2	
Y	39									1	2	
Zr	40									2	2	
Nb	41									4	1	
Mo	42									5	1	
Tc	43									5	2	
Ru	44									7	1	
Rh	45			36						8	1	
Pd	46			Krypton core						10		
Ag	47									10	1	
Cd	48									10	2	
In	49									10	2	1
Sn	50									10	2	2
Sb	51									10	2	3
Te	52									10	2	4
I	53									10	2	5

of orbitals either filled or half filled. This accounts for the slight irregularities at Cr and Cu in Table 2.A. These observations apply to single atoms, and, as we will see, when covalent bonds are formed between atoms, they may be superseded by other considerations.

MOLECULES

So far, we have discussed orbitals in terms of energy levels and the quantum numbers used to describe them. However, molecules have very specific shapes and sizes. The atoms in a molecule are located at definite positions with respect to one another; the bonds are oriented in specific directions. The center-to-center distance between two bonded atoms is called the *bond length*. When two or more atoms are bonded to the same atom, the angle formed by drawing a pair of straight lines from center to center, along the bonds, as shown in Fig. 2.3, is called the *bond angle*. These two quantities, bond length and

Figure 2.3. Bond angle.

bond angle, are specific measurable quantities for any given molecule, and depend both on the atoms involved and on the type of bonding. (Strictly speaking, bond lengths and angles refer to average atomic positions, as thermal energy causes the atoms to vibrate around an equilibrium position. These vibrations have amplitudes and frequencies, and can be described in terms of *force constants*, much as if the atoms were connected by springs. The following discussion will always refer to equilibrium or average distances or angles. Although we use equilibrium distance and average distance interchangeably, they are not exactly the same, because the vibrations are not strictly harmonic. However, the difference is generally so small that many workers in the field of molecular structure do not distinguish between the two, and we shall not do so here.)

In order to understand why molecules have specific spatial configurations, we must look more closely at atomic orbitals from a geometric viewpoint, using the results of quantum mechanics.

The *s* orbitals are spherically symmetric about the nucleus. The

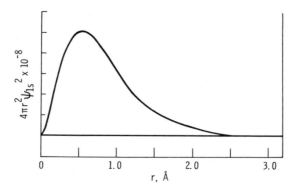

Figure 2.4. Radial probability distribution function for a 1s electron in hydrogen.

distance of highest probability from the nucleus for a 1s electron turns out to be just that calculated from the Bohr theory. The radial probability distribution function for a 1s electron in hydrogen is shown in Fig. 2.4. We can think of the s orbitals in an atom as a series of diffuse spherical shells, the distance from the nucleus of maximum probability for a 2s electron being greater than that of a 1s, a 3s greater than that of a 2s, and so on. The p orbitals have a definite angular dependence. The three p orbitals of any quantum number n have the appearance of three dumbbells directed along three mutually perpendicular axes, as shown in Fig. 2.5. The d orbitals are more difficult to represent geometrically, but they also consist of a series of lobes, and they are highly directional.

It should be kept in mind that quantum mechanics gives a mathe-

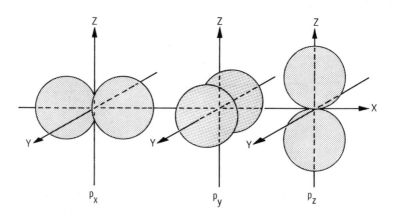

Figure 2.5. Angular dependence of p orbitals.

matical description of the atom. The physical picture we have been discussing in the preceding paragraphs, although derived directly from quantum mechanics, is less exact than the purely mathematical description. However, the physical picture is close to the truth and, since it is much more useful for our discussion of chemical bonding, we will continue to use it. Those who would like to delve into the mathematics will find some of the references listed in the appendix sufficient to satisfy their inclinations.

COVALENT BONDS

Bonding was defined in a general sense in Chapter One, and we saw that this word can be applied to a wide variety of atomic interactions that lead to atomic aggregates of some degree of stability. In this section, we are concerned with *covalent bonds*. These are the bonds that hold atoms together in specific, identifiable, geometric arrangements to form molecules.

The requirements for the formation of a covalent bond can be stated quite simply. All that is needed are two electrons with opposed spins (an *electron pair*) and an available *stable orbital* in each of the two atoms to be bonded. In fact, quantum mechanics tells us that an atom can form such an electron-pair bond with *each* available stable orbital. When we speak of an "available stable orbital," we generally mean an orbital in an outer shell of the atom, so that interpenetration of the bonding orbitals of the two bonded atoms is possible.

The hydrogen atom has only one stable orbital ($1s$) and thus can form only one covalent bond. Carbon, nitrogen, and other atoms in the first row of the periodic table are limited to four covalent bonds, using the four orbitals of the L shell (the $2s$ and the three $2p$ orbitals). This limitation provides the justification for the so-called *octet rule*, in which an atom of the first row of the periodic chart was supposed to be stable when surrounded by eight electrons.

Quantum mechanics also tells us that, in general, each additional electron-pair bond formed in a molecule further stabilizes the molecule, so that the most stable electronic structures of a molecule are those in which all the stable orbitals of each atom are used, either in bond formation or for occupancy by an unshared pair of electrons. Molecules made up of atoms in the first row of the periodic table in general utilize all four orbitals of the L shell (with the sharing of electron pairs being limited only by the number of electrons present). For example, the nitrogen atom in the ammonia molecule, NH_3, with five electrons in the L shell, uses three orbitals for occupancy by the shared electron pairs involved in the formation of the $N—H$ bonds, and the fourth orbital for occupancy by the unshared pair of electrons. Elements in the second row of the periodic table are also generally limited to the formation of four bonds, since the $3d$ orbitals are less stable than the $3s$ and $3p$ orbitals. However, there are many exceptions in the case of the second row elements where five or six bonds are formed, utilizing one or more d orbitals for bond formation. In the other rows of the periodic table, the octet rule still has significance. That is, the general tendency in molecule formation is to have eight electrons in the outer shell of each atom, consisting of four electron pairs in four orbitals, each pair either forming a bond or occupying an orbital as an unshared pair. This is true except in the case of the transition elements, where the use of d orbitals in bond formation becomes the rule, rather than the exception.

If each of two atoms has a stable orbital available and there are a pair of electrons around, the two atoms can form a bond between themselves. The simplest case is the hydrogen molecule. Each hydrogen atom has a stable $1s$ orbital and one electron to contribute. To form a bond, the two orbitals interpenetrate and the pair of electrons are shared by both atoms. A chlorine atom has seven electrons in its M shell, two in the $3s$ orbital, two each in two of the $3p$ orbitals, and one in the third p orbital. Thus, a hydrogen atom and a chlorine atom can get together to form a molecule of hydrogen chloride, HCl, each atom contributing an orbital and an electron to form the bond. Or, two chlorine atoms can get together and form a Cl_2 molecule. These bonds are called *single bonds*, because one pair of electrons and one pair of orbitals are utilized in joining the pair of atoms. Multiple bonds, involving more electron pairs and orbital pairs, will be discussed later. In these examples, each atom involved in bond formation contributed one electron. However, in many cases, one of the atoms contributes an orbital containing an electron pair, and the other atom contributes an empty stable orbital. In this case, the bond is called a *coordinate covalent bond*. This situation fulfills our criteria for covalent bond formation just as well as the previous examples. We will cite many examples of this type of bond formation when we discuss coordination complexes. The main point here is that a bond can be formed provided we have two stable orbitals and an electron pair, regardless of whether one or both of the atoms contribute electrons.

In terms of our electron cloud picture, the bonding electrons are concentrated in the region between the nuclei of the two bonded atoms, where the bonding orbitals interpenetrate or overlap. However, we must remember that electrons do spend some of their time elsewhere in their orbital. Furthermore, since all electrons are the same, and neither we nor the atoms can tell one from the other, the electron originally belonging to one atom spends some of the time moving around the other atom, and vice versa. The two electrons are thoroughly mixed up in the bonding orbitals of the two atoms. This mixing up, or *exchange*, of the two electrons is very important. Quantum mechanical calculations show that this electron exchange contributes greatly to the stability and strength of a chemical bond. It is the simplest example of quantum mechanical *resonance*, and the stability it adds to the bond is called *resonance energy.*

We can perhaps better understand the quantum mechanical meaning of resonance with a simple example. Consider two hydrogen atoms bonded together to form a hydrogen molecule. Let's pretend that we can label the atoms A and B, and their original electrons (1) and (2), respectively. We can write the *structure* of the hydrogen molecule as $A(1) - B(2)$; in other words, each atom is still closely associated with the electron that originally came with it. However, since the electrons are indistinguishable, a structure just as good as the first one is $A(2) - B(1)$, that is, with the electrons interchanged. We could also write structures with both electrons associated with one of the atoms, such as $A(1)(2)^- - B^+$ or $A^+ - B(1)(2)$, but such *ionic* structures are not very important in the hydrogen molecule, where both bonded atoms are the same. None of these structures violates the Pauli principle. The hydrogen molecule is said to *resonate* between all these structures (mostly the first two).

Unfortunately, resonance is a somewhat misleading term for this phenomenon, because it implies an alternation from one structure to another with some particular frequency, like the swing of a pendulum or the oscillation of a spring. However, in quantum mechanical terms, it simply means that we can't get the right answer to a problem, such as an energy calculation, unless we include all these structures in the calculations, each weighted according to its probability (like breaking a complicated problem into several pieces, each of which is solvable, then recombining the partial answers to get the whole answer), so that the concept of resonance is essentially mathematical. For our purposes, the important thing to remember is that the electrons forming a bond do get mixed up, and that this mixing up or exchange adds to the stability of the bond. An analogy may be useful: A mule is neither a horse nor a donkey, but is one separate non-oscillating animal with elements of a horse and a donkey!

In a molecule such as H_2 or Cl_2, the two atoms are the same and each exerts an equal influence on the shared electrons. In a molecule such as HCl, however, the chlorine atom exerts a greater attraction for the shared electrons than does the hydrogen atom. The center of charge of the negative electron cloud in the HCl molecule is shifted toward the chlorine atom relative to the center of charge of the positive nuclei. The HCl molecule therefore behaves as if the hydrogen atom has a slight positive charge and the chlorine atom has a slight negative charge. Such a molecule is a *polar* molecule, with a *dipole moment,* and the bond is said to have *partial ionic character.*

The degree to which different atoms exert a greater or lesser attraction for electrons is called *electronegativity.* Relative electronegativity values, as deduced by Pauling, are shown in Table 2.B. The more electronegative an atom is, the greater its attraction for electrons. If two atoms are joined in a covalent bond, the difference in electronegativity between the two atoms is a measure of the degree of polarization of the molecule, and the degree of ionic character in the bond. Fluorine is the most electronegative element, followed by oxygen, then nitrogen and chlorine. Bonds formed by these elements with elements farther to the left in the periodic table will be highly polar. If the electronegativity difference between two atoms is *very* great, they tend to exist as separate positive and negative ions, the more electronegative atom taking complete possession of one or more electrons from the less electronegative atom. Such atoms are held together by *ionic bonds,* which in essence are simple coulombic attraction rather

TABLE 2.B

The Electronegativity Scale

Li	Be	B	C	N	O	F
1.0	1.5	2.0	2.5	3.0	3.5	4.0
Na	Mg	Al	Si	P	S	Cl
0.9	1.2	1.5	1.8	2.1	2.5	3.0
K	Ca	Sc	Ge	As	Se	Br
0.8	1.0	1.3	1.8	2.0	2.4	2.8
Rb	Sr	Y	Sn	Sb	Te	I
0.8	1.0	1.2	1.8	1.9	2.1	2.5
Cs	Ba	La	Pb	Bi	Po	At
0.7	0.9	1.1	1.8	1.9	2.0	2.2

than the interpenetration of orbitals and electron sharing. Bonds between the alkali metals and halogens fall into this class. Ionic bonds will be discussed in more detail in Chapter Three.

MORE BOND PROPERTIES

It is known experimentally that the bonds between some pairs of atoms are much stronger than the bonds between other pairs. These differences are conveniently expressed in terms of *bond energy*. The bond energy may be defined as the difference in energy between the molecule A-B and two isolated atoms A and B. Expressed a little differently, it can be considered as the net amount of energy required to break the bond between A and B to yield two separate atoms. Thus the strength of the bond is directly proportional to the magnitude of the bond energy. Bond energies are usually expressed in kilocalories per mole; that is, the number of kilocalories of energy required to break Avogadro's number (6.024×10^{23}) of bonds. The bond energy for any particular pair of atoms is very nearly the same in any molecule containing that pair of bonded atoms, provided it is the same type of bond (single bonds, in our present discussion). For example, the average bond energy of the four $C—H$ bonds in methane is the same as the average bond energy of the ten $C—H$ bonds in butane.

Using thermochemical and spectroscopic data, it is possible to derive a table of bond energies, such as that shown in Table 2.C for

TABLE 2.C

Energy Values for Single Bonds (Kcal/mole)

Bond	Bond energy	Bond	Bond energy
H—H	104.2	N—H	93.4
C—C	83.1	O—H	110.6
Si—Si	42.2	S—H	81.1
Ge—Ge	37.6	H—F	134.6
Sn—Sn	34.2	H—Cl	103.2
N—N	38.4	H—Br	87.5
P—P	51.3	H—I	71.4
As—As	32.1	C—N	69.7
O—O	33.2	C—O	84.0
S—S	50.9	C—F	105.4
Se—Se	44.0	C—Cl	78.5
Te—Te	33	C—Br	65.9
F—F	36.6	C—I	57.4
Cl—Cl	58.0	Si—F	129.3
Br—Br	46.1	N—F	64.5
I—I	36.1	N—Cl	47.7
C—H	98.8	P—Cl	79.1
Si—H	70.4	P—Br	65.4
		P—I	51.4

single bonds. A glance at this table shows that the energy values for the various single bonds cover a range of about a factor of three, that is, from about 40 to about 120 kilocalories per mole. It is also interesting to note that the energies are higher (the bonds are stronger) between atoms whose electronegativities show the greatest difference.

TABLE 2.D

Single Bond Covalent Radii for Atoms (Å)

C	N	O	F
0.772	0.70	0.66	0.64
Si	P	S	Cl
1.17	1.10	1.04	0.99
Ge	As	Se	Br
1.22	1.21	1.17	1.14
Sn	Sb	Te	I
1.40	1.41	1.37	1.33

For example, bonds involving fluorine with elements near the middle of the periodic table are among the strongest listed in Table 2.C.

As mentioned previously, the region of highest probability for occupancy by an electron (the region of highest electron density in our smeared-out electron cloud analogy) gets farther from the nucleus of an atom as we go to the higher principal quantum numbers. Thus, the heavier atoms occupy more volume than the lighter ones and, since it is the outer orbitals that are used in bonding, bond lengths will be greater in the heavier elements. Hence, in the series HCl, HBr, HI, the bond distance increases in the order HCl < HBr < HI; the bonding orbitals are in the *M* shell for chlorine, the *N* shell for bromine, the *O* shell for iodine, and the *K* shell for hydrogen.

The bond distance between two atoms can be divided into two parts, corresponding to a *covalent'radius* for each atom. It is not too surprising, on the basis of the preceding discussion, to find that the covalent radius for a given atom is very nearly constant in any molecule whose atom is covalently bonded. Thus, if we have a table of covalent radii, we can get a very good estimate of the covalent bond distance for any pair of atoms simply by adding the two covalent radii. Variations of more than a few percent from this additivity are rare. A list of such radii for covalent single bonds is given in Table 2.D. Similar tables can be derived for other bonding situations, such as multiple bonds and ionic bonds. Within each class, the additivity relationship is reasonably accurate.

POLYATOMIC MOLECULES

In *polyatomic* molecules (those containing three or more atoms) bond angles are largely determined by the atomic orbitals involved in the formation of the bonds. Since the directions of maximum electron density of the *p* orbitals in an atom are at an angle of 90° to one another, we would expect the bonds formed by an atom utilizing its *p* orbitals to have an angular separation of about 90°. The experimentally determined bond angles for a number of simple molecules where *p* orbitals are involved in bonding are listed in Table 2.E, and we see that the values are indeed close to 90°. The large angles found in H_2O and NH_3 can be regarded as due to coulombic repulsion between the hydrogen atoms, caused by the high degree of polarity in

TABLE 2.E

Molecule	Bond Angle	Experimental Value
H_2O	H—O—H	$104.45° \pm 0.10°$
NH_3	H—N—H	$107.3° \pm 0.2°$
H_2S	H—S—H	$92.2° \pm 0.1°$
PH_3	H—P—H	$93.3° \pm 0.2°$
H_2Se	H—Se—H	$91.0° \pm 1°$
AsH_3	H—As—H	$91.8° \pm 0.3°$
H_2Te	H—Te—H	$89.5° \pm 1°$
SbH_3	H—Sb—H	$91.3° \pm 0.3°$

the O—H and N—H bonds. However, they can also be described as hybrid sp^3 orbitals, as discussed below for carbon, with a lone pair of electrons in one or two orbitals.

HYBRID ORBITALS

In many cases, an atom will have available s and p or s, p, and d orbitals of similar energies for use in bond formation. For example, carbon has four stable orbitals (the $2s$ and three $2p$ orbitals) and four electrons in the L shell. The basic requirements for the formation of four bonds are therefore satisfied. In the normal state of the carbon atom, the electrons are distributed in the L shell, as shown in structure I of Fig. 2.6. One of the $2s$ electrons could be promoted to the vacant p orbital to yield structure II, so that one might expect the carbon atom to form an s bond and three p bonds. If the carbon atom

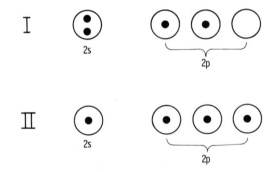

Figure 2.6. Possible electron distribution in carbon.

actually formed bonds in this manner, then a molecule such as methane, CH_4, would have two kinds of C—H bonds. It is known experimentally, however, that all four C—H bonds in methane are the same, and are arranged symmetrically about the carbon atom, the bonds being directed toward the corners of a regular tetrahedron with the carbon atom at the center. The arrangement of bonding orbitals in Fig. 2.6 obviously could not produce such a symmetrical structure for methane.

In order to resolve this dilemma, we again draw on the results of quantum mechanics. In general, a wave function for a system can be constructed by adding together other functions; the wave function for the normal state of the system will then be the one that minimizes the energy of the system. The energy of a system consisting of a carbon atom and four attached atoms is minimized by making the bond energies as large as possible. It is found that a bond orbital formed by combining s and p orbitals in certain ways can make stronger bonds than either an s or p orbital alone. Such a combination is called a *hybrid* orbital. It is possible to construct four such orbitals which maximize the total bonding energy for the carbon atom, and it is found that these four orbitals are exactly equivalent and that the electron densities in these orbitals are concentrated in directions that make the tetrahedral angle of 109° 28′ with one another. These hybrid orbitals are called *tetrahedral* or sp^3 orbitals.

The carbon atom can form other types of hybrid orbitals, and these will be discussed later. An important point to remember is that if an atom can form stronger bonds (thereby minimizing the energy of the molecule as a whole) by hybridizing its bonding orbitals, it will generally do so.

TRANSITION METALS

We recall that the $3d$ orbitals are very similar in energy to the $4s$ and $4p$ orbitals (Fig. 2.1). We also recall that the transition metals are characterized by partially filled d orbitals. We might expect these conditions to result in the formation of d bonds by the transition metals. The formation of pure d bonds, however, is rare. Instead, when d orbitals take part in bond formation, they tend to do so in the form of d-s-p hybrid orbitals.

The transition metal complexes are good examples of bond formation using *d-s-p* hybrids. We will use the ferrocyanide and ferricyanide complex ions as examples. These ions consist of an iron atom bonded to six cyanide groups, located at the corners of a regular octahedron, with the iron atom in the center. All six bonds are equivalent. (The rules for bond formation in a polyatomic ion are the same as those in neutral molecules.)

The electronic arrangement in outer shells of the Fe^{3+} and Fe^{2+} ions are shown in Fig. 2.7.

Since the electrons in the *d* orbitals can be paired to leave two empty *d* orbitals for use in bond formation in the cyanide complexes, the electronic arrangements in the iron atoms become those in Fig. 2.8, so that six orbitals are available for bond formation. These orbitals combine to form six equivalent d^2sp^3 or *octahedral* hybrid orbitals, having high electron densities in the octahedral directions. Note that these bonds are examples of the coordinate covalent bonds mentioned earlier, in that both electrons involved in the bond come from the carbon atom of the cyanide group, the iron supplying empty orbitals in which these electron pairs are shared. The pronounced angular distribution of these octahedral hybrids results in the formation of very strong bonds.

Referring again to Fig. 2.8, we notice that there is an unpaired electron occupying a *d* orbital in the iron atom of the ferricyanide ion, $Fe(CN)_6^{3-}$. Since an electron is a spinning charged particle, it has a magnetic moment. When electrons are paired in an orbital, the spins must be antiparallel (Pauli principle), so the magnetic moments of the two electrons exactly cancel one another. When there are unpaired electrons in a molecule or ion, the substance will have a magnetic moment which can be measured. Furthermore, the magnitude of this moment is proportional to the number of unpaired electrons, so magnetic measurements are often useful for determining the correct

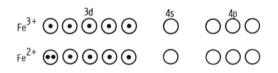

Figure 2.7. Electronic arrangements in Fe^{3+} and Fe^{2+} in the ground state.

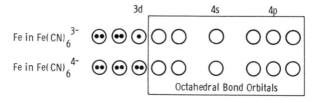

Figure 2.8. Electronic arrangements in Fe^{3+} and Fe^{2+} when octahedral bonds are formed.

electronic structure for an atom where two or more possibilities exist. The iron atom in the ferrocyanide ion has no unpaired electrons; hence its magnetic moment is zero.

Another type of common *d-s-p* hybrid orbital is the *dsp²* or *square planar* arrangement, found in bivalent nickel complexes, such as $Ni(CN)_4^{2-}$. If we fill in the orbitals in the bivalent nickel ion as we did with the iron, we find that we need four of the $3d$ orbitals for electron pairs, leaving one d orbital and the $4s$ and three $4p$ orbitals available to form bonds. By hybridizing these orbitals, it is found that four strong bonding orbitals can be formed. These are directed to the corners of a square, with the Ni^{2+} in the center. The third p orbital is not used.

These *d-s-p* hybrid orbitals are used for covalent bond formation in many different complexes of iron and nickel as well as in other transition metals whose electronic structures are suitable, substituting $4d$ or $5d$ orbitals where appropriate in the heavier elements. Other types of hybrids involving d orbitals are formed by certain elements, but they are less common than the two we have discussed. Anyone interested in pursuing the subject will find further reading references in the appendix.

MULTIPLE BONDS

So far, we have been considering covalent single bonds, where one electron pair is shared by two participating atoms, each atom contributing one orbital for bond formation. However, many elements, particularly those in the first row of the periodic table, can form double or triple bonds, where two or three pairs of electrons are shared, each atom contributing a like number of orbitals. Since the carbon atom forms an almost infinite number of compounds in a great variety of bonding arrangements, we will emphasize this remarkable atom in our discussion.

Unfortunately, there is no universal agreement among workers in the field with respect to the precise structure of a double or triple bond. By and large, the empirical data available for molecules containing multiple bonds can be explained in several ways. Certainly, very many factors are important in determining the structure of such molecules, and the relative importance of each factor is difficult to assess. As more precise structural data become available, the theoretical concepts involved will be clarified. It should be pointed out that even for such a relatively simple molecule as ethylene, shown in Fig. 2.9, a complete *a priori* quantum mechanical calculation is not possible at the present time.

The orbitals involved in carbon-carbon double bonds in molecules such as ethylene have usually been described in two different ways. According to one description, the carbon atoms use the $2s$ orbital and two of the $2p$ orbitals to form three sp^2 hybrid orbitals. These three orbitals lie in a plane with an angle of 120° between any pair. The axis of the third, unhybridized, p orbital is perpendicular to the plane of the three sp^2 hybrids. The double bond is formed by overlap of one of the hybrid orbitals from each carbon atom to form a so-called σ (sigma) bond and by "sideways" overlap of the unhybridized p orbitals to form a so-called π (pi) bond. The two remaining sp^2 hybrid orbitals on each carbon atom are used for bonding to other atoms, hydrogen in the case of ethylene. The resulting structure is shown schematically in Fig. 2.10. The p orbital has lobes, both above and below the plane of the sp^2 orbitals, and the π bond, of course, involves both lobes.

In order to form a triple bond, as in acetylene, HC≡CH, according to the σ-π bond theory, the carbon atom uses the $2s$ orbital and one

Figure 2.9. Structure of ethylene.

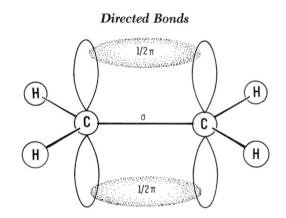

Figure 2.10. Schematic arrangement of orbitals for sp^2 hybridization in ethylene.

of the $2p$ orbitals to form two sp hybrid orbitals, directed along a straight line on opposite sides of the carbon atom. This leaves two unhybridized p orbitals on each carbon atom whose axes are perpendicular to each other and to the axes of the sp hybrid orbitals. A triple bond is formed by using an sp hybrid from each atom to form the σ bond and the two p orbitals from each atom to form a pair of π bonds. The remaining sp hybrid orbital is used for a bond with another atom. Thus, a triple bond, as in acetylene, can be represented schematically as in Fig. 2.11.

The other major theory of multiple bond formation, the "bent bond" theory, is somewhat simpler to visualize. According to this

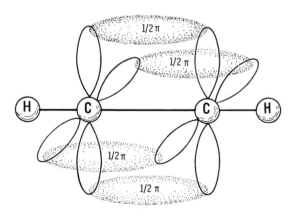

Figure 2.11. Schematic arrangement of orbitals for sp hybridization in acetylene.

theory, the orbitals of the carbon atom are always tetrahedral hybrids. To form a double bond, two of the orbitals from each carbon atom overlap. The geometry requires that the orbitals overlap at an angle with respect to their axes, and that is why the resulting bond is called a "bent" bond. If we imagine a tetrahedron circumscribed around each carbon atom with the four sp^3 orbitals directed toward the corners, then the double bond is equivalent to the two tetrahedra sharing an edge. Similarly, a triple bond is equivalent to the two tetrahedra sharing a face.

This can perhaps be more easily visualized by using models, for example, cork balls to represent the center atoms and colored pins set in the balls at the proper angles to represent the orbital directions.

Without going into all the arguments pro and con, and the various modifications to the theory which have been proposed, let's consider a few experimental facts in relation to the predictions of the two descriptions of multiple bonds. If we examine the molecular geometry predicted by the two theories, we find that the magnitude of the angle between a double bond and an adjacent single bond—for example, the angle α in propylene shown in Fig. 2.12—should be 120°, according to the σ-π bond theory and 125.27°, according to the bent bond theory. Here the experimental evidence is favorable to the bent bond theory. This angle in propylene, and in most other molecules, is very close to 125°. An exception is ethylene, where the C=C—H angle is 121° or 122°. Bond angles, however, are often distorted by intramolecular repulsions. We must remember that no matter how we represent them on paper, atoms occupy space and there is a distance of closest approach where they begin to repel one another. The atoms within a molecule can therefore crowd one another, so that we must be careful in drawing absolute conclusions on the basis of bond angles alone.

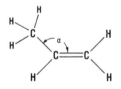

Figure 2.12. Structure of propylene.

The normal bond lengths for carbon-carbon single bonds, double bonds, and triple bonds are approximately 1.54 Å, 1.33 Å, and 1.20 Å, respectively. The geometry of the bent bond theory predicts values very close to these for the multiple bonds relative to the single bond, as can easily be verified with a model or some practical use of high school geometry. The σ-π bond theory does not yield relative bond lengths quite so simply, but we would certainly expect such a variation in bond distance with a change in the hybridization of the orbitals used to form the bond.

Another bit of experimental data that can be used to support either theory is the variation of C—H bond lengths depending on whether the carbon atom is involved in single, double, or triple bonds. The approximate values for these bond lengths are, respectively, 1.10 Å, 1.08 Å, and 1.065 Å. These differences are significantly greater than the error involved in a large number of molecular structure investigations. Since we would not expect the covalent bonding radius of the hydrogen atom to vary in these three situations (it has only one stable orbital and can form only *s* bonds under normal conditions), we could argue that this variation implies a variation in the hybridization of the carbon atom. However, we could also argue that the difference is due to the molecule minimizing its total energy by balancing maximum overlap, which decreases the energy, against intramolecular repulsion, which increases the energy. A hydrogen atom bonded to a carbon atom engaged in a triple bond, as in acetylene, has little spatial competition relative to three hydrogen atoms bonded to a carbon atom engaged in a single bond, as in ethane. This spatial competition would be relieved by stretching the bond length to some degree, so that the C—H bond lengths in the three situations might be expected to be in the observed sequence: ethane longer than ethylene longer than acetylene.

It may seem that this discussion leans somewhat in favor of the bent bond theory for multiple bonding. However, it should be obvious that neither side has clean, clear-cut arguments—on the basis of experimentally determined molecular structures, at any rate. Indeed, at least one investigator has been able to explain qualitatively the differences in bond length and bond angle from molecule to molecule solely on the basis of intramolecular repulsions (or the lack of them).

AROMATIC BONDS

Another type of bonding, largely reserved for the carbon atom, is that found in aromatic ring compounds, the simplest example of which is benzene, C_6H_6. The benzene molecule consists of six carbon atoms bonded together in the form of a planar six-membered ring, with a hydrogen atom bonded to each carbon atom. All of the carbon-carbon bonds are identical.

Utilizing the available orbitals and electrons, we can write two exactly equivalent structures for benzene, as in Fig. 2.13. Quantum mechanical calculations show that the wave function which leads to the minimum energy for the benzene molecule is a combination of the wave functions corresponding to each of the structures indicated in this figure. Here we have an example of quantum mechanical resonance involving the whole molecule, rather than a single pair of bonding electrons, as in our previous example. Again, the amount by which the energy of the molecule is reduced, compared with either of the structures shown in Fig. 2.13 alone, is called the resonance energy of benzene.

The bonding in benzene is perhaps best visualized in terms of σ and π bonds, where the ring skeleton and the C—H bonds involve sp^2 hybrid orbitals, and the remaining three pairs of electrons are evenly distributed among the six p orbitals oriented perpendicular to the plane of the ring, with lobes above and below, as shown in Fig. 2.14. These electrons are said to be *delocalized,* since they do not belong to any particular pair of atoms, but rather are shared equally by all six carbon atoms. Since all the C—C bonds in benzene are the same, and the bonds are neither double bonds nor single bonds, the modern notation for representing a benzene ring is the simple diagram of Fig. 2.15, it being understood that there is a carbon atom at each corner, with a hydrogen atom bonded to it.

Nitrogen has three stable orbitals available for bonding, and it can participate in aromatic ring formation along with carbon, as in the molecules shown in Fig. 2.16. Since the nitrogen atom has five electrons in its L shell, in these molecules its fourth orbital is used to contain an unshared electron pair, instead of bonding to a hydrogen atom.

Some molecules, such as the naphthalene, anthracene, and phenanthrene in Fig. 2.17, are made up of several benzene rings fused

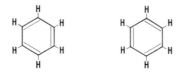

Figure 2.13. Equivalent structures for benzene.

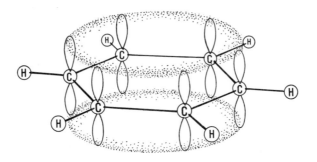

Figure 2.14. Schematic arrangement of orbitals in benzene.

Figure 2.15. Simple notation for benzene ring.

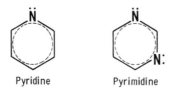

Pyridine   Pyrimidine

Figure 2.16. Structures of pyridine and pyrimidine.

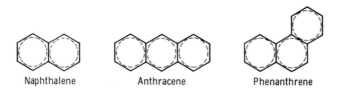

Naphthalene   Anthracene   Phenanthrene

Figure 2.17. Structures of naphthalene, anthracene, and phenanthrene.

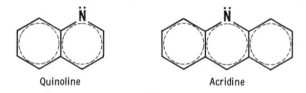

Figure 2.18. Structures of quinoline and acridine.

together. Such ring systems can also have one or more nitrogen atoms substituting for the carbon atoms in the rings, and then we have the structures shown in Fig. 2.18. Of course, the structure of all these ring systems must be planar.

In this chapter we have outlined some of the basic principles of covalent bonding. Of course, we have barely scratched the surface of this subject; many interesting topics have been omitted. We hope, however, that this small taste will stimulate an appetite for further reading.

3

Collusion

IN THE PRECEDING CHAPTER, we discussed the properties of atoms that make bonding possible, and considered in some detail the directed covalent bond. Now we turn our attention to how ions or atoms or molecules unite to form the finite masses of matter that we see and use every day; in particular, we will be concerned with the ordered arrays called *crystals*. As we will see, many crystals are built up by a series of covalent bonds linking one atom with the next throughout the entire structure, as is the case with diamond. Similarly, many crystals are built up entirely of ions, positive and negative, so that the forces that hold the crystal together are essentially coulombic, as in the case of sodium chloride. We must now consider another force of attraction—actually a group of forces—which do not involve bond formation in the sense that we have discussed bonds so far, but which are very important in many crystals. Indeed, these are the only forces that hold together many substances, such as crystals of most organic molecules and the rare gases. This group of forces of attraction are lumped together under the name *Van der Waals forces*.

Van der Waals forces include dipole-dipole interactions between polar molecules, inductive effects, and various other weak interactions. These forces will be discussed in more detail in Chapter Five, but for

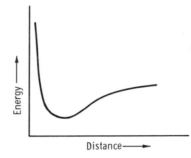

Figure 3.1. Curve representing potential energy as a function of distance of separation for a pair of atoms.

our present purposes, we need remember only two things: First, these forces provide much weaker linkages than those involving covalent or ionic bonds, corresponding to bond energies of a few kilocalories at most, and usually much less. Second, Van der Waals interactions include not only attractive forces, but also repulsive forces which become important only at very short distances. The combination of attractive and repulsive forces can be represented by an energy-distance curve, as shown in Fig. 3.1. The minimum in this energy curve corresponds to the most stable configuration, and the inter-atomic distance at which this minimum occurs is a measure of the *size* of the atoms, that is, how close together two atoms can get when *not* joined by a chemical bond. This distance can be expressed in terms of a radius, just as we defined a covalent bond radius in Chapter Two. Such "non-bonded" radii are called *Van der Waals radii*. The Van der Waals radius of a given atom is much larger, of course, than the covalent bonding radius for that atom, roughly by a factor of two.

Let's now examine a few representative crystal structures from the point of view of bonding, beginning with covalently bonded crystals. Diamond is an example of a crystal held together by covalent bonds that tie carbon atoms together throughout the crystal lattice, so that the diamond crystal, in one sense, is like a giant molecule made up entirely of carbon atoms. Each carbon atom is bonded to four other carbon atoms arranged at the corners of a regular tetrahedron. The carbon atoms are thus in the sp^3 state of hybridization, and the C—C—C bond angle is the tetrahedral angle, 109°28′. Silicon and germanium have the same structure. The strong three-dimensional

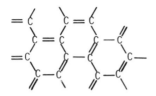

Figure 3.2. A possible structure for a layer in graphite.

covalent bonding makes these substances very hard, diamond being the hardest substance known.

Some other substances are covalently bonded in two dimensions—graphite, for example. The graphite crystal consists of planar layers of covalently bonded carbon atoms. The distance between these layers is 3.40 Å, too large for any covalent bonding, so that the layers are held together by the weak Van der Waals forces. This is why graphite comes apart so easily that it is a commonly used lubricant, although water vapor or oxygen are needed to split the layers apart. Each graphite layer consists of carbon atoms arranged in hexagons. Each carbon atom can form four bonds but has only three neighbors, so we can write many resonance structures, as indicated in Fig. 3.2.

If we consider the carbon-carbon bonds in benzene as $1\frac{1}{2}$ bonds, or as having 50 percent double bond character, then we can easily see that the carbon-carbon bonds in graphite are $1\frac{1}{3}$ bonds, having 33 percent double bond character. Thus, each layer in graphite is like a giant two-dimensional molecule.

Some crystals consist of atoms held together by covalent bonds in one direction to form long chains, with the chains, in turn, being held together by Van der Waals forces. Tellurium, whose structure is shown in Fig. 3.3, is an example. A tellurium crystal will tend to shatter if we

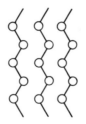

Figure 3.3. Bonding arrangement in the tellurium crystal.

try to cleave it perpendicular to the chain direction, but it cleaves quite easily parallel to the chains.

IONIC CRYSTALS

We have purposely reserved a discussion of ionic bonding for this chapter, because, as we will see, it is more realistic to talk about ionic bonds in terms of crystals rather than molecules. An ion is simply an atom or molecule that bears a net charge, positive or negative, which is an integral multiple of the electronic charge.

Let's consider a pair of monatomic ions, sodium, Na^+, the cation, and chloride, Cl^-, the anion. The electronic structure of both is that of a noble gas, that is, a sodium atom ionizes by losing its lone $3s$ electron, leaving it with the electronic structure of neon, and a chlorine atom ionizes by adding an electron to complete its M shell, so that it has the electronic structure of argon. Quantum mechanical calculations show that the electronic distributions for ions with noble gas structures (or those with eighteen outer electrons, such as Zn^{2+}, which has eighteen electrons completely filling the $3s$, $3p$, and $3d$ orbitals) are spherically symmetrical. Thus, the interaction of two such ions is independent of direction.

At large distances, the sodium ion and the chloride ion will attract one another by coulomb interaction of their charges with the potential function

$$\frac{Z_1 Z_2 e^2}{r_{12}},$$

where Z_1 and Z_2 are the number of charges on the ions (both unity in this example), e is the electronic charge, and r_{12} is the distance between the ions. As the ions are brought closer together, so that their outer electron shells begin to overlap, a repulsive force comes into play to oppose the coulombic attraction, the two ions coming to equilibrium at some equilibrium interatomic distance.

The potential energy of the crystal per Na^+Cl^- ion pair can be written

$$V = -\frac{Ae^2}{R} + \frac{Be^2}{R^n}, \tag{3.1}$$

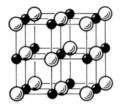

Figure 3.4. The sodium chloride structure.

where R is the smallest interatomic distance in the crystal. The first term on the right side of Eq. 3.1 represents the attractive forces, and the second term represents the repulsive forces. The repulsive forces fall off very rapidly with distance, the exponent n having a value of about 9 for most crystals. The constant A is called the *Madelung constant*. In a sense, it is a measure of the binding energy of ions in a crystal. The value A for an isolated Na^+Cl^- ion pair is unity.

If we now add other sodium and chloride ions to our initial pair, a sodium chloride crystal is built up with the structure shown in Fig. 3.4, in which the small spheres represent Na^+ and the large spheres Cl^-. Examining this structure, we see that each Na^+ has six equidistant Cl^- for nearest neighbors, and each Cl^- has six equidistant Na^+ for nearest neighbors. This ion packing arrangement lowers the energy per ion pair in the crystal by about 75 percent below the energy of isolated Na^+Cl^- ion pairs, as is evidenced by a Madelung constant of 1.7476 for sodium chloride. This great stability of the crystalline array of ions accounts for the fact that sodium chloride in the form of discrete NaCl molecules can exist only under very extreme conditions. For this reason, we must discuss the bonding in ionic compounds in terms of crystals rather than in terms of molecules. Furthermore, the concept of a specific bond energy for a pair of atoms is less meaningful here than it is for covalent bonds, because the forces acting on any specific ion are determined by the entire crystalline environment.

Although coulombic forces account for most of the ionic bond energy, they are not the only forces involved. Van der Waals forces also make a small contribution, as do polarization effects (distortion of the electronic distribution in one ion due to the field of its neighbors). Some degree of covalent bond character might also exist, although we would expect this to have more significance with ions of higher atomic weight

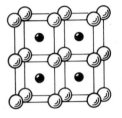

Figure 3.5. The cesium chloride structure.

where stable d orbitals might be utilized. All of the alkali halides crystallize in the sodium chloride structure, except cesium chloride, bromide, and iodide, which have the cesium chloride structure shown in Fig. 3.5, where the dots represent Cs^+ and the spheres Cl^-. At first glance, it appears that the cesium chloride structure contains an excess of halide; note that each small cube contains a cesium ion at its center and has $\frac{1}{8}$ share of each of 8 halide ions at the corners, so that in the extended crystal there are equal numbers of both anions and cations. This structure differs from the sodium chloride structure in that each cation has 8 anions as nearest neighbors, and each anion has 8 cations as nearest neighbors, instead of the 6 nearest neighbors found in the sodium chloride structure.

We can build up similar crystals, using pairs of divalent ions instead of monovalent ions. For example, MgO has the sodium chloride structure, as do most of the alkaline earth chalcogenides. The principles involved are exactly the same, except that each ion is doubly charged.

It is possible to calculate a set of ionic radii for various ions, although the procedure is not as simple and straightforward as in the case of covalent bond radii. Values for a few common ions are given in Table 3.A. However, if we compare sums of these radii for various ion combinations with the values for interatomic distances actually observed in crystals—for example, all the alkali metal halides having the sodium chloride structure—we find some rather large deviations, particularly for the lithium halides. Furthermore, it is not possible for *any* single set of radii to account for all the observed interatomic distances in the alkali metal halides.

An important reason for this lack of additivity involves simple spatial considerations. If we look at the atomic arrangement in a face of a crystal such as LiBr, using the ionic diameters given in Table 3.A (see Fig. 3.6),

TABLE 3.A

Crystal radii of ions (Å)

O^{2-}	F^-	Li^+	Rb^+	Be^{2+}	Sr^{2+}	B^{3+}	Y^{3+}
1.40	1.36	0.60	1.48	0.31	1.13	0.20	0.93
S^{2-}	Cl^-	Na^+	Ag^+	Mg^{2+}	Cd^{2+}	Al^{3+}	In^{3+}
1.84	1.81	0.95	1.26	0.65	0.97	0.50	0.81
Se^{2-}	Br^-	K^+	Cs^+	Ca^{2+}	Ba^{2+}	Sc^{3+}	La^{3+}
1.98	1.95	1.33	1.69	0.99	1.35	0.81	1.15
Te^{2-}	I^-	Cu^+	Au^+	Zn^{2+}	Hg^{2+}	Ga^{3+}	Tl^{3+}
2.21	2.16	0.96	1.37	0.74	1.10	0.62	0.95

we see that the Br^- ions are in contact with one another, while the Li^+ ions still have plenty of room. The repulsive forces acting between the bromide ions when they come in contact override the attractive forces between the lithium ions and the bromide ions at a point where, on the basis of ionic radii, the Li^+ and Br^- ions have not yet reached mutual contact. Simple geometry shows that this situation will occur in sodium-chloride type structures whenever the ratio of the cation radius to the anion radius is less than $\sqrt{2} - 1 = 0.414$, assuming the ions to be hard spheres. Even in cases where the anions are not in actual contact in the hard sphere sense, the anion-anion repulsions, arising when the cation-anion size difference is large, can be sufficiently great to cause the equilibrium interionic distances observed in the crystal lattice to be greater than those predicted from the derived ionic radii. It is the balancing out of all the attractive and repulsive forces among all the ions, such that the energy of the system as a whole is minimized, which determines the actual interionic spacings in the crystal. These factors come into play in other crystals besides those having the sodium chloride structure, but they are perhaps more obvious here, not only because the sodium chloride structure is a common one, but also because

Figure 3.6. Crowding of anions in LiBr.

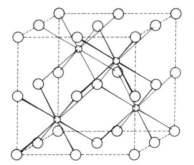

Figure 3.7. The fluorite structure.

the simplicity of this structure permits very accurate experimental determinations of the distances involved.

In building up a crystal of an unsymmetrical valence type of substance, such as compounds of the form MX_2, the forces involved are the same as those in the sodium chloride case. However, the structure becomes somewhat more complicated. A common structure for compounds of this type is that of fluorite (CaF_2) shown in Fig 3.7.

As compounds get more complicated (for example, mica, $KAl_3Si_3O_{10}(OH)_2$) their crystal structures become quite complex. Simplifications can often be made, however, in discussing such structures, by noting that certain substructures or groups of atoms always occur in certain arrangements. This fact is of great practical use to the x-ray crystallographer when he is determining the complete structure of a complicated crystal. For example, we know that the ferricyanide complex ion has octahedral symmetry, as discussed in Chapter Two. Therefore, the structure of potassium ferricyanide will consist of $Fe(CN)_6^{3-}$ octahedra and K^+ ions in the ratio of $1:3$, all packed together to form a stable configuration.

In the silicon dioxide structure, each silicon atom is surrounded by four oxygen atoms in a tetrahedral arrangement. In order to maintain the stoichiometric ratio $1:2$ for silicon and oxygen, each oxygen atom must act as the corner of two SiO_4 tetrahedra, so that we can consider the silicon dioxide structure as built up of an infinite array of SiO_4 tetrahedra with shared corners, as indicated in Fig. 3.8.

Many minerals contain silicon and oxygen in addition to other elements. In these complex structures, the silicon is generally located in

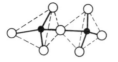

Figure 3.8. The relationship of silicon and oxygen atoms in SiO_2.

the center of a tetrahedron of oxygen atoms. Aluminum usually occurs in a similar group, that is, tetrahedra of oxygen atoms with the aluminum located in the center. A model of the structure of sodalite, $Na_4Al_3Si_3O_{12}Cl$, which contains both SiO_4 and AlO_4 tetrahedra, is shown in Fig. 3.9.

Figure 3.9. Model of the structure of sodalite.

In the preceding discussion of mineral structures, we have used the word "atom" instead of "ion" because some of the bonds, for example, the Si-O bonds, are perhaps best considered as covalent bonds with a high degree of ionic character, arising from the electronegativity difference between Si and O atoms. These complex mineral structures usually contain bonds with a variety of characteristics. For example, imagine the sodalite structure as a network of SiO_4 and AlO_4 tetrahedra joined by polar covalent bonds, in which Na^+ and Cl^- ions are placed in such positions as to maximize the stability of the structure. Notice that a count of electrons shows that the AlO_4 tetrahedra average one negative charge each, so that the electrical neutrality of the structure is maintained.

MOLECULAR COMPOUNDS

When substances that exist as discrete molecules crystallize, the individual molecules that come together to form the crystal are held together by Van der Waals forces. We might expect such crystals to come apart rather easily, compared with ionic crystals or with covalently bonded lattices, such as diamond. If we use melting points as a rough measure of crystal cohesive forces, we find plenty of support for this conclusion. The melting point of methane is $-184°C$, compared to $801°C$ for sodium chloride, and $2000°C$ for corundum, a form of aluminum oxide with a Madelung constant of 25. However, we find many organic compounds consisting of larger molecules that have melting points in the range of $100°C$ to over $200°C$, which indicates that the forces holding these molecules together in a crystal can be quite substantial. The reason for this stability lies in the number of atoms in one molecule in contact with atoms in an adjacent molecule. A molecule with 20 or 30 atoms, or more, will have a large number of Van der Waals contacts with other molecules in the crystal, so that even though the attractive forces between any two atoms may correspond to energies of less than a kilocalorie per mole, the total energy of association between any two molecules may be several tens of kilocalories. These associative forces can be sufficiently strong that some compounds will decompose before they melt; that is, one or more covalent bonds in the molecule will break before the forces holding the molecules together in the crystal are disrupted. Thus, wood (cellulose) does not melt when heated. Even in the absence of air, it breaks down to form water vapor, carbon, and various chemical compounds.

METALS AND SEMICONDUCTORS

The crystal structures of the metallic elements are for the most part simple, usually involving a problem of packing spheres. The bonding in metallic elements and intermetallic compounds, however, is the least understood of all the types of bonding we have discussed. A complete theory of the metallic bond must account for certain properties exhibited in varying degrees by the substances we call metals, properties such as high electrical and thermal conductivity, metallic luster, and ductility, as well as the chemical properties of metals. By and large, the theory of metals at its current state of development can do this only qualitatively, although advancements are coming at a rapid rate. We should mention that, historically, the investigation of bonding in metals and intermetallic compounds has been grossly neglected, especially when compared with the effort expended on the carbon atom and its compounds.

In the bond types discussed in this chapter and in the preceding one, we have been able to "assign a home" to all the outer electrons of the atoms forming the bonds. In other words, we could locate them, usually as pairs, in specific orbitals either on one atom or ion, or in a pair of atomic orbitals used to form a covalent bond, or at least in a small group of orbitals, as in benzene. But in order to account for the properties of metals, not all of the electrons in a metal can be localized; some of the electrons must be "free"—able to move easily throughout the crystal lattice.

In 1916, the Dutch physicist H. A. Lorentz developed a theory of metals which could account for many of their properties. He considered a metal as a crystalline arrangement of hard spheres, the metal cations, with free electrons moving through the interstices. Thus, sodium would consist of Na^+ ions, magnesium of Mg^{2+} ions, and so on, each ion contributing one, two, or more "free" electrons, depending on its valence. Among other things, the free electrons "cement" the ions together in their crystalline arrangement. In recent years, through the application of quantum mechanics and modern statistical theory, physicists have developed the free electron model to a point where it can explain semi-quantitatively some of the properties of metals, and they have tied together metals, semiconductors, and insulators with the modern band theory of solids. However, the calculations involved are extremely complex. Often, assumptions must be made which seriously limit the usefulness of the results. It is only in the past few years, with the availability of large computers, that such calculations could be approached in even a roughly quantitative fashion.

The physicist is primarily interested in the electrons in a solid, particularly the unbound electrons. In the band theory, described below, the properties of solids are related to energy levels in the crystal and the electronic populations of such energy levels. The actual atoms in the crystal are important only because they determine the periodic potential in which electrons move in the crystal and because they determine the positions of the main energy levels on the energy scale. If we wanted to, we could discuss the band theory in its present state of development without mentioning a single specific chemical element or compound.

A somewhat different, and more chemical, approach to metals and metallic bonding is presented by Linus Pauling, and this reference will be found in the appendix. We will not discuss the Pauling approach in detail here. Suffice it to say that it retains the valence bond as the principal binding agent for metal atoms in a crystal, adding the concept of a metallic orbital and resonance among many valence bond structures. Pauling's methods enable him to correlate interatomic distances in metals and intermetallic compounds in a logical manner.

The two approaches mentioned above should not be considered as rivals. The free electron concept and the band theory explain the electronic properties of metals and solids in general, and the requirements of modern technology will certainly assure the further development of this approach. However, anyone primarily interested in atomic arrangements and interatomic distances in crystals might find the Pauling approach more useful.

It is interesting to compare insulators, semiconductors, and metals from the viewpoint of band theory. Since the energy states for a free electron depend on its complete crystalline environment, the physicist is generally concerned not with particular atoms but with the entire crystal on a statistical basis. When appropriate calculations are performed, it is found that the energy levels that can be occupied by electrons in any given solid consist of a series of discrete bands. Energy levels between these bands cannot be occupied by electrons, and such regions are called *forbidden energy gaps*. In a band only partially filled, the electrons can move rather easily, and such a band is called a *conduction band*. One that is completely filled is called a *valence band*.

Let's now consider a rather crude analogy to illustrate the simplest points of the band theory. Imagine a stack of checkerboards, with spaces in between. Each checkerboard represents all the positions in all of the energy levels in a given band which can be occupied by electrons. The vertical separations between the boards correspond to forbidden energy gaps. Now we start filling the squares (black and red) with checkers (electrons), beginning with the bottom board (lowest energy band). We can readily see that if a board is completely filled, there are no positions left in which to move any checkers on that board. However, if we have a few checkers left over to put on another board, these checkers have plenty of positions available and can easily be moved.

In Fig. 3.10, the differences between insulators, semiconductors, and metals are illustrated. The shaded areas represent regions occupied by electrons. If a solid has a certain number of energy bands completely filled, and others completely empty, it is classed as an insulator. On the other hand, if a solid has an energy band that is only partially filled, it is a metal. The illustrations in Fig. 3.10 really apply only to absolute zero. At higher temperatures, some electrons will be excited from the highest filled band into the conduction band. The extent to which this occurs depends on the width of the forbidden energy gap; the width of this gap provides the main distinction between an insulator and an intrinsic semiconductor. If the gap is large, say several electron volts,

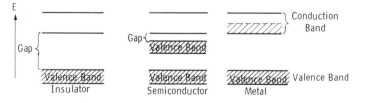

Figure 3.10. The band picture of insulators, semiconductors, and metals.

so few electrons are excited into the conduction band at any practical temperature that the solid remains an insulator, in our usual sense of the word, at all temperatures. Diamond, with a forbidden gap of 7 ev, is an example. However, if the gap is small, less than 1 ev, then the number of thermally excited electrons can be considerable at ordinary temperatures, and such materials—germanium and silicon, for example—are called *intrinsic semiconductors.*

If an electron in a semiconductor is thermally excited into the conduction band so that it is free to move about the crystal lattice, it leaves behind a positive charge in the region of the atom which gave up its electron. This positive charge is called a *hole.* Now, an electron from a neighboring atom can jump into this vacant position, or hole, leaving behind a positive charge on that neighboring atom. Such a process can continue throughout the lattice and is equivalent to the positive charge, or hole, moving through the lattice. Thus, in an intrinsic semiconductor, an electric current is carried by both electrons and holes, and these exist in equal numbers. This situation can readily be visualized in terms of our stack of checkerboards.

It should be clear at this point that the magnitude of the electrical conductivity of a given intrinsic semiconductor depends only on the temperature. In order to use such materials in devices, such as diodes and transistors, it is necessary to control the conductivity. This is normally accomplished with *impurity doping.*

Let's consider a crystal of silicon. Silicon has the diamond structure, each Si atom joined to four others tetrahedrally by electron-pair bonds which we will represent as in Fig. 3.11. Now we substitute a group-five element, such as arsenic, for some of the silicon atoms, as shown in Fig. 3.12. We see that arsenic has one more electron than is needed to form its four bonds with Si atoms. This electron is rather weakly held, and it requires very little energy to set it free to move throughout the lattice. In band theory terminology, the arsenic atoms are *donors,* and their existence in the lattice gives rise to *donor levels* close to the conduction band, shown schematically in Fig. 3.13. In such a doped semiconductor, the bulk of the electrical conduction is done by electrons; it is called an *n-type* semiconductor. The magnitude of the electrical conductivity can be readily controlled by adjusting the concentration of impurity atoms when the silicon crystal is growing.

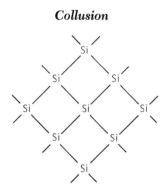

Figure 3.11. Schematic picture of the silicon lattice.

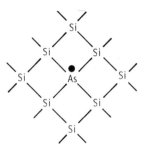

Figure 3.12. Schematic picture of an arsenic-doped silicon lattice.

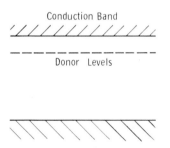

Figure 3.13. Band picture of a semiconductor doped n-type.

If, instead of atoms of a group-five element, we put atoms of a group-three element, such as aluminum, into a silicon lattice, we find we have one too few electrons for forming four bonds with neighboring silicon atoms, as indicated in Fig. 3.14. In order to form a fourth bond, an electron must be drawn from a nearby atom, creating a hole. This hole can move through the crystal lattice, just as in the intrinsic case.

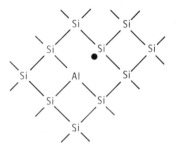

Figure 3.14. Schematic picture of an aluminum-doped silicon lattice.

Thus, the aluminum atoms are called *acceptors*, and they introduce *acceptor levels* close to the valence band. This situation is shown diagrammatically in Fig. 3.15. Since the bulk of the electrical conduction in this kind of doped semiconductor takes place through the movement of holes, it is called a *p-type* semiconductor. Again, the magnitude of the electrical conductivity is determined by the concentration of acceptor atoms in the lattice.

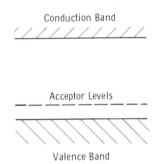

Figure 3.15. Band picture of a semiconductor doped p-type.

In this chapter, we have pointed out some of the aspects of bonding which are particular to the macroscopic aggregates of materials called crystals, including some elements of the band theory and its relation to bonding in semiconductors. Actually, we have touched rather lightly on these subjects, emphasizing only those points that will be needed for the discussions that follow. Some of the references listed in the appendix treat these topics in greater depth.

Bonds in
Transition

CHEMICAL REACTIONS involve breaking bonds and reforming them to yield products that differ from the starting compounds. Equations written to describe such reactions generally show the reactants and the products, as well as the weight relationship between them. In this chapter, we are going to expand the study of these equations to include the mechanisms by which reactions occur. We will try to find out what intermediate pathways reactions take in proceeding to the final products.

In the experimental study of reaction mechanisms or paths, a complete description of the reacting system is not practical or even possible on the basis of Heisenberg's uncertainty principle. However, we can establish important landmarks (or intermediate states) on the reaction path. The theory of absolute reaction rates, largely developed by Henry Eyring and his students, has been important in the study of reaction mechanisms, and centers attention on such intermediate or transition states. Reaction rates are related to the structure of these transition states, so that the measurement of the speed of reactions is a means of determining the mechanisms involved.

Besides studying reaction speeds, or *kinetics*, there are other powerful experimental methods of determining the mechanisms. It is now possible to trace the course of individual atoms in a reaction with the use of isotopes as labels. Also, knowledge of the geometry of a molecule enables the chemist to relate the products to the reactants on the basis of how they may fit together in space. These are known as *stereochemical studies*. In the sections to follow, we will present in more detail examples and ideas used in describing reaction mechanisms.

COLLISION THEORY

Collision between molecules is generally necessary for reaction. This is the case even in the decomposition of a single molecule, where the energy required is usually obtained by a collision process. An important factor in determining the speed of chemical reactions is therefore the frequency of collision of the reacting molecules.

In addition to collisions, before reacting, a minimum energy must first be absorbed by a molecule to weaken or activate bonds which eventually are to be broken. This energy of activation is required even when the reaction causes an over-all release of energy on completion. The energy content of a molecule during the course of reaction is illustrated in Fig. 4.1. The concept that molecules must be activated before reacting was postulated by the Swedish chemist Svante Arrhenius on

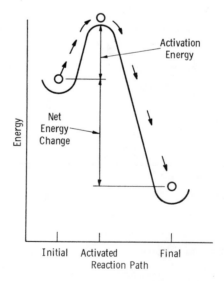

Figure 4.1. Activation energy barrier, ΔE.

the basis of his studies of the effect of temperature on reaction rates. He found that the speed of simple reactions increases with temperature at a greater rate than expected by increases in collision frequency with temperature alone, and is proportional to the factor $e^{-\Delta E/RT}$, where ΔE is the activation energy per mole, R is a constant, and T is the absolute temperature. This factor gives the probability that a molecule possesses energy in excess of the amount ΔE. It turns out that many reactions have activation energies of about 50 kcal/mole, and this leads to a general result that the speed of reactions is often doubled for an increase in temperature of $10°C$, an old empirical rule. This will give an idea of the great sensitivity of reaction rate to the temperature.

In order to get a better insight into the role of collision in chemical reactions, we will calculate a chemical reaction rate on the basis of simple collision and activation of molecules before reaction. The *law of mass action*, discovered by Guldberg and Waage in 1867, states that the speed of a chemical reaction is proportional to the "active masses" of the reactants. In the case of gases and solutions, the active mass is given by the concentration, C. Thus, for the general reaction

$$aA + bB \rightarrow \text{products,}$$

the reaction rate equals

$$KC_A{}^aC_B{}^b,$$

where K is a constant, called the *rate constant*, and C_A is the concentration of A. The sum of the number of molecules of each kind involved in the reaction $a + b$ is defined as the *order of the reaction*. For the simplest gas reactions, this sum gives the number of molecules that collide on activation. This may not be true for more complex reactions, in which several intermediate steps may appear. We are interested in calculating the *rate constant K*, which is defined by this reaction rate equation. Let's consider the reaction of the decomposition of gaseous hydrogen iodide:

$$2HI \rightleftharpoons H_2 + I_2.$$

The rate expression is:

$$\text{rate of disappearance of HI} = K \times (C_{HI})^2.$$

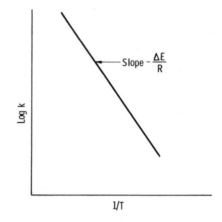

Figure 4.2. Arrhenius plot.

Since the rate is proportional to the number of collisions and the fraction of activated molecules, the expression for K is

$$K = Ze^{-\Delta E/RT},$$

where Z is the number of HI molecules that collide per second. From the kinetic theory of gases, Z is calculated at $556°K$ to be 6.0×10^{31} molecules/cc/sec. The activation energy is calculated from the experimentally observed reaction rate constant from the slope of a graph of log K against $1/T$, which is called an *Arrhenius plot,* as shown in Fig. 4.2. The activation energy obtained in this way is 44,000 cal/mole, and

$$e^{-\Delta E/RT} = e^{-44,000/1.99 \times 556} = 5.2 \times 10^{-18}.$$

This is the fraction of HI molecules with an energy greater than the activation energy. The rate constant K is

$$K = Ze^{-\Delta E/RT} = 6.0 \times 10^{31} \times 5.2 \times 10^{-18}$$
$$= 3.1 \times 10^{14} \text{ molecules reacting/cc/sec.}$$

This value compares reasonably well with the experimental value of 2.1×10^{14} molecules reacting/cc/sec.

Similar calculations have been successful for reactions in solutions as well; however, many examples exist where unreasonably low results are obtained. This requires introducing a probability factor P into the pre-exponential term to account for the requirement of preferred orientation on collision and special states of motion before activation results. These conditions may be illustrated by the reaction

$$A\text{-}B + C \rightarrow A + B\text{-}C.$$

The collision orientation,

$$A\text{-}B \quad C,$$

is favorable for activation, while the orientation

$$C \quad A\text{-}B$$

is not. Also, if as C approaches A-B the vibration of this bond causes extension and weakening, reaction may be more likely than when the bond between A and B is compressed. The energy obtained by collision must be transferred to the bond that undergoes reaction. This energy transfer may be an inefficient process for a complicated molecule with many vibrational and rotational modes.

The *absolute reaction rate theory* accounts for the probability factor by assuming that the reactants are in chemical equilibrium with the activated molecules. On the basis of this assumption, the activation energy term ΔE may be considered to include a term called the *change in the entropy of activation,* ΔS. This measures the change in the degree of organization in the transition state, as compared to the unactivated reactant state. The probability factor then can be calculated using this term. In principle, the activation energy and the activation entropy can be calculated from quantum mechanics for the transition state, assuming a given structure. Thus, experimental reaction rates can be checked against postulated transition states in order to determine a reaction mechanism.

The entropy of activation is an important concept of the absolute reaction rate theory. Let's now illustrate its application to mechanism studies. Entropy is a measure of randomness or disorganization; the fewer the restrictions on motion of the activated molecules, the higher the entropy of activation. Logically then, if a decrease in entropy is involved in forming the activated complex, that is, if a great degree of organization is required, the probability of formation of a transition state on collision will be lower than the probability of a transition state of greater entropy of activation. This will result in a lower reaction rate. Gas reactions of the type

$$A + B \rightleftharpoons [A\text{-}B]^* \rightarrow A\text{-}B,$$

known as *additions*, generally involve a decrease in entropy on forming the activated complex. This is because, on collision of two molecules to form an activated complex, independent motion of each molecule is lost, so that severe restriction on freedom of motion results. Often the asterisk (*) is used to indicate the activated complex.

In the same way, formation of a cyclic transition complex involves a decrease in entropy or a negative activation entropy, because freedom of rotational motion about single bonds is lost. The *rearrangement*, or *isomerization* reaction

$$CH_2{=}CH{-}CH_2{-}O{-}CH{-}CH_2 \rightarrow CH_2{=}CH{-}CH_2{-}CH_2{-}\overset{\overset{\displaystyle O}{\|}}{C}H$$

proceeds through formation of a ring for a transition complex, shown in 4.A. Studies of the rate of this reaction have shown that the acti-

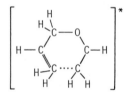

4.A. Cyclic transition state.

vation entropy is negative, in agreement with the mechanism involving a cyclic transition complex.

Crowding of the structural groups in a molecule can lower the

$$CH_3CH_2O^- + R\,CH_2I \rightarrow \left[CH_3CH_2O\text{---}\overset{\displaystyle H}{\underset{\displaystyle H\ \ R}{\overset{\displaystyle \diagdown}{C}}}\text{---}I \right]^* \longrightarrow CH_3CH_2O\text{-}CH_2R + I^-$$

4.B. Activated complex.

entropy of activation. In the reaction (4.B), the entropy of activation for the crowded restricted-motion case, where R is shown in 4.C, is

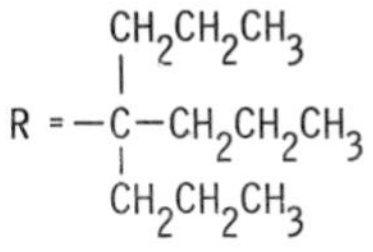

$$CH_2CH_2CH_3$$
$$|$$
$$R = -C-CH_2CH_2CH_3$$
$$|$$
$$CH_2CH_2CH_3$$

4.C. Tripropyl methane group.

lower by about a factor of two than that observed for the case where R = H.

ISOTOPES AND STEREOCHEMISTRY

How isotopes have been used as "labels" in investigating reaction mechanisms is exemplified by the study of the reaction between benzoic acid and methyl alcohol. The product, methyl benzoate, may be formed by rupture of a carbon-hydrogen bond of the acid or of the alcohol, together with a hydrogen-oxygen bond-splitting of the other

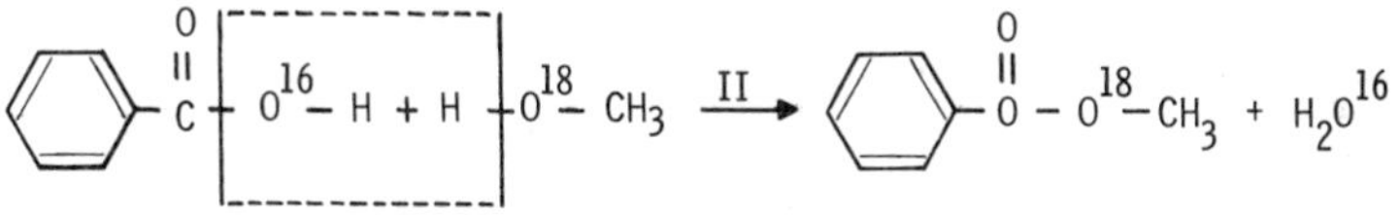

4.D. Acid H split, mechanism I.

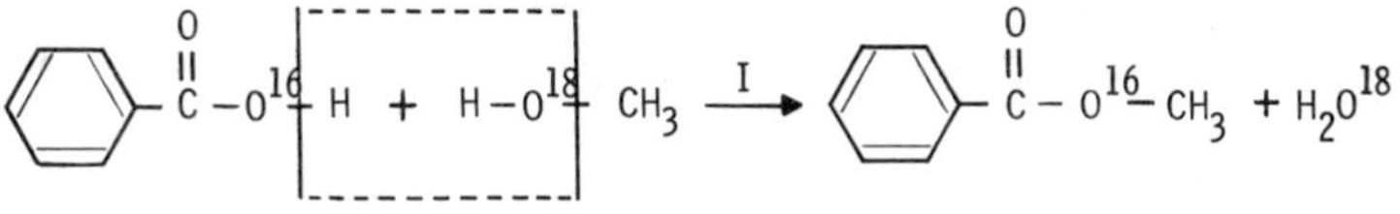

4.E. Acid OH split, mechanism II.

reactant, as shown in 4.D and 4.E. To distinguish between these two mechanisms, methyl alcohol was used in the reaction, with the heavy oxygen isotope O^{18} serving as a label. The oxygens of the benzoic acid are O^{16}. Analysis of the products, using a mass spectrometer, showed the O^{18} to be incorporated in the methyl benzoate, rather than in the water formed. Thus, reaction mechanism 4.D was shown to occur with the carbon-oxygen bond of the alcohol being attached, and mechanism 4.E does not occur.

This same type of reaction—the combination of an organic acid with an alcohol—demonstrates the importance of stereochemistry in understanding mechanisms. It has been observed that adding groups to the benzene ring adjacent to the

group in benzoic acid drastically reduces the rate of reaction. The rate is reduced independent of the electronic properties of the substituent added. Thus, addition of groups, with either electron-attracting or electron-donating bonds, has the same reaction-inhibiting effect. In view of this, it is believed that there is a stereochemical effect operating here.

A stereochemical explanation can be derived if we assume that the transition state is formed preferentially by collision of alcohol molecules which occur from a direction perpendicular to the plane defined by the

group. The effect of crowding this group by ring substituents is to move its plane out of the plane of the ring. Adjacent substituents will then be in the line of perpendicular approach to the group and will block its path, as shown in Fig. 4.3.

Mechanisms of substitution or *displacement* reactions between a polar covalent bond and an attacking ion have been worked out in some detail. This has been possible because reactions performed with optically active molecules (those whose solutions rotate the plane of polarized light) have allowed chemists to gain insight into conformation changes that occur in molecules as a result of reaction. Let's consider the general reaction:

$$C^- + A\!\!-\!\!B \rightarrow \bar{C}\!\!-\!\!\overset{+}{A}\!\!-\!\!\bar{B} \rightarrow C\!\!-\!\!A + B^-$$

As C^- approaches A, the bond between A and B is weakened, and the transition complex involves a structure with A bonded with equal

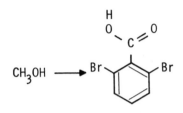

Figure 4.3a. Blocked approach.

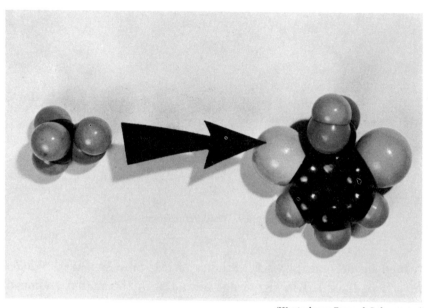

(Westinghouse Research Laboratories.)

Figure 4.3b. Sterically hindered reaction.

strength to C and B. The reaction proceeds to completion with rupture of the A-B bond and the formation of a new C-A bond. The most logical direction of attack for C^- is from the rear, away from B, whose negative polarity would repel C^-.

The Russian chemist Paul Walden observed that hydrolysis of optically active chlorosuccinic acid resulted in the formation of malic acid that showed optical activity in the reverse sense to that of the starting compound. This indicated that the conformation of the molecules was changed on reaction; in other words, the molecule was

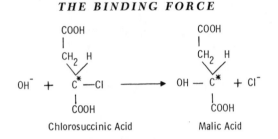

4.F. Walden inversion.

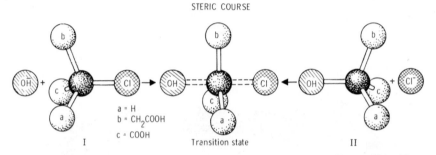

STERIC COURSE

a = H
b = CH$_2$COOH
c = COOH

I   Transition state   II

(From *Advanced Organic Chemistry*, by Louis F. Fieser and Mary Fieser.
New York: Reinhold Publishing Corp., 1961. Adapted and redrawn by permission.)

Figure 4.4. Walden inversion.

turned inside out. (See 4.F.) Studies of this process, called *Walden inversion*, have led to significant advances in the understanding of reaction mechanisms. (See Fig. 4.4.)

SOLUTION REACTIONS

Many chemical reactions take place with reactants present in the dissolved state. The basis for modern ideas on electrically conducting or electrolyte solutions was given by the Swedish chemist Svante Arrhenius, who showed that physical and electrical properties of these solutions could be explained in terms of the dissociation of substances into electrically charged species or ions on entering solution. The ions are free to move in the solution and thus carry electric current. Strong electrolytes or those compounds that form very highly conducting solutions are completely dissociated, whereas the weaker electrolytes

$$CH_3\overset{\overset{\textstyle O}{\|}}{C}-OH \rightleftharpoons CH_3\overset{\overset{\textstyle O}{\|}}{C}-O^- + H^+$$

4.G. Dissociation equilibrium of acetic acid.

or less conducting solutions contain undissociated molecules in equilibrium with dissociated ions. (See 4.G.)

To get a better idea of the details of chemical reactions that occur in solution, let's now look into the process of dissolution, first considering dissolution of an ionic solid, such as NaCl, into water. Strong electrostatic forces bind the positive sodium ions and negative chloride ions into a stable cubic lattice. (See Chapter Three.) To disrupt the lattice and disperse the ions into solution requires that the energy of the crystal lattice be overcome in some way. This is done by reaction with the solvent to give ions that are bound firmly to the solvent molecules. The reaction is known as *solvation*. It is the energy of the solvation reaction that overcomes the lattice energy, causing the crystal to decompose into ions in solution. These ions are not free, but are firmly bonded to solvent molecules. Sodium chloride dissolved in water results in the formation of four electrostatic bonds of the ion-dipole type between Na^+ and the negative oxygen end of four water dipoles. Similarly, the negative chloride ion binds to the positive hydrogen end of the water dipoles, as shown in Fig. 4.5. In addition to solvent molecules, ions of opposite charge will also be attracted to the dissolved ion so that, as it moves in solution, it will carry with it a loosely bound aggregate or atmosphere of opposite-charged ions, in addition to its solvation sheath. (See Fig. 4.6.) Thus, collision

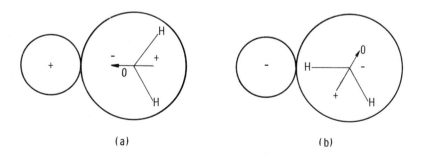

(a)   (b)

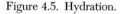

Figure 4.5. Hydration.

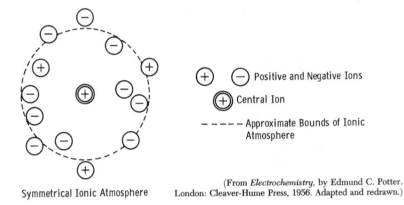

Symmetrical Ionic Atmosphere

(From *Electrochemistry*, by Edmund C. Potter. London: Cleaver-Hume Press, 1956. Adapted and redrawn.)

Figure 4.6. Solvation sheath.

processes in solution require the penetration of a counter-ion atmosphere and rearrangement of bound solvent molecules.

As a result of this dissolution mechanism, ionic solids are usually most soluble in polar liquids or liquids in which charge separation occurs. Thus the great solvent power of water may be attributed to its highly polar nature. This causes the water not only to bond, or solvate, foreign ions readily but also to bond to itself, or *associate*. In this case, positively charged hydrogens of one water molecule form electrostatic bonds to the negative oxygens of an adjacent molecule. These bonds are dipole-dipole interactions, which amount to between 5 and 10 percent of the strength of covalent bonds. The importance of such bonding to the structure of water and other associated liquids (such as liquid ammonia and liquid hydrogen fluoride) is clearly shown by its effect of raising the boiling point and the freezing point to higher values than would be expected from the periodic trend shown in Fig. 4.7.

This type of bonding—between hydrogen and negative species, such as oxygen—is known as *hydrogen bonding*; it is of key significance in the structure of proteins and other compounds of biological importance, as described in detail in Chapter Seven.

The dissolution of covalently bonded solids that form molecular crystals involves overcoming a lower lattice energy due to Van der Waals forces, as explained in Chapters Three and Five. Thus, lower solvation energies are required. In this case, neutral molecules are removed from the crystal lattice and are solvated, often by forming hydrogen bonds.

The dissolved molecules, together with a sheath of solvent molecules, move in the solutions. Dissolution of compounds whose bonding is intermediate in type between ionic and covalent results in a solution containing ions as well as undissociated molecules in equilibrium. At higher concentrations (higher density of ions in a given volume) the increased chances for collisions between ions of opposite sign result in relatively greater amounts of associated ions to form neutral molecules than at lower concentrations, where dissociation and ionization are more complete.

Association reactions of ions in solution generally require removal and replacement of solvent from the solvation sheath. The simplest example of this type of reaction involves the exchange of solvent molecules between a solvated metal cation and the bulk solvent. Measurements of solvent exchange rates have recently been made by such diverse techniques as the use of isotopes and ultrasonic absorption spectra. It has been found that in aqueous solutions the alkali metal ions (Li^+, Na^+, K^+, Rb^+, Cs^+) and the alkaline earth ions (Ca^{2+}, Sr^{2+}, Ba^{2+}) have high exchange rates for solvated water. Low rates of exchange have been

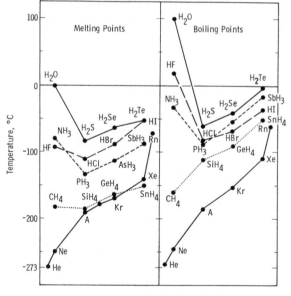

(From *General Chemistry*, by Linus Pauling. San Francisco: W. H. Freeman and Company, 1953. Adapted and redrawn.)

Figure 4.7. Anomalous boiling and melting points.

observed for Mg^{2+} and for most of the divalent ions of the first transition series.

In the case of association of solvated cations with negative ions,

$$M^+ + L^- \rightarrow ML,$$

the rates are fast for alkali and alkaline earth ions and also show variations with the type of associating ion, often referred to as a *ligand*, as well as with the electrostatic potential (ratio of the charge to the ion size) of the cation. This indicates that the rate-controlling step here is the attachment of the anion, rather than desolvation. For Mg^{2+} and first transition series divalent ions, the association rates are all the same, so that in each case a common mechanism of slow desolvation controls the rate of association.

ELECTRON TRANSFER PROCESSES

Electron transfer reactions are familiarly known as *oxidation-reduction* reactions, when electrons are transferred between ions of different atomic number. Reduction corresponds to a gain of electrons, while oxidation refers to a loss of electrons. When electron transfer occurs between ions of the same atomic number, the reaction is called an *electron exchange*, and no net chemical effects are observed. It is therefore necessary to use isotopic labeling in order to study the course of these reactions. For example, the electron exchange between ferrous and ferric ions in solution has been studied by using radioactive trivalent iron, $*Fe^{3+}$ and natural Fe^{2+}:

$$*Fe^{3+} + Fe^{2+} \rightarrow Fe^{3+} + *Fe^{2+}.$$

These reactions are of considerable interest, because the lack of chemical changes simplifies the theoretical treatment so that their study is useful in obtaining a basic understanding of electron-transfer processes in general.

Investigation of electron-transfer reactions has revealed two important types of mechanisms: (1) direct electron tunneling, and (2) ligand-bridged transition states.

Very fast rates are observed in the direct tunneling mechanism, and it is believed that when the two exchanging species approach closely and make contact, the electron is transferred by a quantum mechanical process of tunneling. Here, as a consequence of the uncertainty principle (it is impossible to completely specify the position of a particle), there is a finite probability that the electron exists on the product side of the energy barrier. Thus, the electron can tunnel, or leak through the barrier, without the necessity of surmounting it. Examples of exchange reaction couples considered to proceed by a tunneling mechanism are:

$$[Mn(CN)_6]^{3-}, [Mn(CN)_6]^{4-}; \quad [W(CN)_8]^{3-}, [W(CN)_8]^{4-};$$
$$[IrCl_6]^{2-}, [IrCl_6]^{3-}.$$

Although the principle of tunneling is general, it is of significance only for very light particles, such as electrons. Tunneling by particles heavier than electrons, except in nuclear reactions, is most likely not important, because of the strong influence of the mass. Such a mechanism, however, has been suggested to account for the high mobility of protons in ice and water.

A ligand-bridged transition state mechanism occurs in the reduction of coordinated trivalent cobalt ions by chromous ions:

$$[Co(NH_3)_5X]^{2+} + Cr^{2+} + 5H_3O^+ \rightarrow [Cr(H_2O)_5X]^{2+} + Co^{2+} + 5NH_4^+$$
$$X = F^-, Cl^-, I^-, NCS^-, N_3^-, CH_3COO^-,$$
$$C_3H_7COO^-, \text{(crotonate, succinate, oxalate, maleate)}.$$

It has been shown that the transition state is

$$(H_3N)_5Co—X—Cr(H_2O)_5.$$

Significantly, the oxalate and maleate anions in the list of X groups provide a continuous path of conjugated π-bonds between the metal ions, and thus allow electron transfer to occur at a rate about 100 times faster than for those groups that do not have this structural feature. (See 4.H and 4.I.)

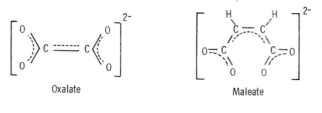

Oxalate   Maleate

4.H. Oxalate ion.   4.I. Maleate ion.

ACIDS AND BASES

Other important reactions in solution are those of acids and bases. The concept of acid and base reactions has been continuously used since the seventeenth century as a classification of reactions. The type of reactions that fall into this category has changed, however, as knowledge of underlying chemical principles has expanded. A very general definition of acids and bases used today has been given by G. N. Lewis, who considers acids to be those compounds that serve as electron acceptors in chemical reactions, whereas bases are electron donors. This description is not dependent on the presence of protons in a solvent, but it also includes the familiar description of acid-base reaction in aqueous solution; it involves the reaction of a hydrogen ion, an electron acceptor, from an acid with a hydroxyl ion, an electron donor, of a base to form water and a salt.

The Danish chemist Johannes Brønsted gave a very useful description of acid-base reactions, although it is less general than that of Lewis. Brønsted defined acids as proton donors and bases as proton acceptors. Since the free proton does not exist in solution but undergoes a solvation reaction, the role of the solvent is emphasized in the Brønsted classification. The proton in aqueous solutions is generally considered to be solvated by four water molecules, $H_9O_4^+$. (See Fig. 4.8.) (It is still general usage, however, to write H_3O^+ or H^+ in equations.) Thus, water acts as a base by associating with the proton. The importance of the solvent may be seen in the case of nitric acid. In water, this compound is one of the familiar strong acids; in liquid hydrogen fluoride, however, HNO_3 is a base! It accepts protons from

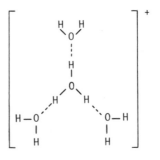

Figure 4.8. Hydrated proton.

the acid HF. The following equations symbolically describe this behavior.

$$HNO_3 + 4H_2O \rightarrow H_9O_4^+ + NO_3^-$$
acid base

$$HNO_3 + HF \rightarrow H_2NO_3^+ + F^-.$$
base acid

Acid-base reactions in water involve *proton transfer processes*, which have been found to be unusually fast. Electrical conductivity measurements have shown that both H^+ and OH^- ions are very highly mobile species in water. Also, activation energies for acid-base reactions are quite low and are interpreted to indicate that the rate of the transfer process is controlled by a collision frequency. In solution, this type of reaction is called *diffusion controlled*. The model used to account for the unusual speed of these reactions involves the hydrogen-bonded structure of water. Proton and also hydroxide ion transfers take place by shifts of protons along hydrogen bonds, without the need for reorganizing the solvation sheath, as in other ionic processes in solution. The mechanisms for proton transfers along hydrogen bonds for hydrogen and hydroxyl ion reactions are shown in 4.J and 4.K.

4.J. Proton transfer reaction.

4.K. Hydroxide ion transfer reaction.

CATALYSIS AND CHAIN REACTIONS

An important property of acids and bases is their ability to alter the speed of many chemical reactions, or *catalyze* them. It has long been observed that the rates of certain reactions are proportional to either the hydrogen ion or the hydroxyl ion concentration in solution, even though acid or base is not involved in the over-all reaction equation, that is, no acid or base appears as a product or a reactant. The action of acids and bases in such a case is to accelerate a reaction by causing it to proceed by a different and easier mechanism. The over-all reaction is unchanged, but a different transition state is used so that the activation energy for the reaction is lowered. We can see, roughly, how this works, if we consider that attachment of a hydrogen ion to a molecule in a transition state attracts electrons toward it, causing a withdrawal of electron density from other parts of the molecule, thus weakening the reaction bonds.

An example of acid catalysis, in the generalized Lewis concept, is the reaction between benzene and methyl chloride. Charles Friedel and James Crafts found that electron acceptor compounds or acids, such as $AlCl_3$, $AlBr_3$, and BF_3, are effective catalysts, as indicated in 4.L. The catalyst operates here by forming an addition compound, or *adduct*, with CH_3Cl, as shown in 4.M. The bond between carbon and chlorine is weakened by the electron withdrawing action of $AlCl_3$, so that its attack on benzene is facilitated.

Now let's take a look at some gas reactions. We saw earlier that the decomposition of HI showed simple bimolecular collision and activation

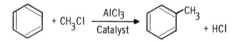

4.L. Friedel-Crafts reaction.

4.M. Friedel-Crafts adduct.

kinetics. The analogous reaction between hydrogen and bromine, on the other hand, does not follow a simple rate law. A completely different mechanism, known as a *chain reaction*, is involved. Analysis of the experimentally determined rate equation indicates the following course of reaction:

$$Br_2 \rightarrow 2Br \cdot \text{ (chain-starting reaction)}$$

$$\left. \begin{array}{l} Br \cdot + H_2 \rightarrow HBr + H \cdot \\ H \cdot + Br_2 \rightarrow HBr + Br \cdot \\ H \cdot + HBr \rightarrow H_2 + Br \cdot \end{array} \right\} \text{ (chain-transfer reactions)}$$

These reactions are repeated, until the bromine atom is finally lost by the chain-ending reaction:

$$2Br \cdot \rightarrow Br_2 \text{ (chain-ending reaction)}$$

Chain reactions are generally characterized by the presence of *free radicals* as chain initiators. These contain an unpaired valence electron and are usually highly reactive. The electron is extremely reactive and will dimerize, or react with another radical or a metal with great speed in order to pair its spin. The unpaired electron of the free radical is indicated by a dot in the reactions given above.

The reaction of hydrogen and chlorine also follows a chain mechanism, and here the chain-initiating chlorine atoms may be formed quite efficiently by the absorption of light of wavelengths below 4758 Å, where the spectrum changes from molecular absorption to dissociation. The photochemical primary process in the reaction is:

$$Cl_2 + h\nu \rightarrow 2Cl \cdot$$

Many gas reactions that are possible theoretically are too slow to be practical. Such reactions, however, can be made to proceed cleanly and rapidly by exposing the reactants to the surface of a solid catalyst. The synthesis of ammonia from nitrogen and hydrogen, for example, requires an iron catalyst. Today most gas reactions used in preparation chemistry are performed with the aid of solid catalysts. Specific chemical combination between gases and solid surfaces is indicated by dependence of the type of chemical reaction on the nature of the catalytic surface. For example, at about 300°C and one atmosphere pressure, ethyl alcohol can decompose in two ways (4.N), depending on the catalyst used. Copper and other metal catalysts cause removal

4.N. Catalytic decomposition of ethyl alcohol.

of hydrogen, whereas alumina and other oxides bring about a dehydration reaction. The difference in catalytic action can be explained by the way in which alcohol is attached to the surface of the catalyst, as indicated in Fig. 4.9. The concept of surface compound formation

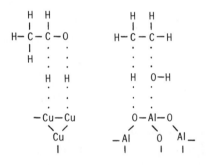

Figure 4.9. Chemisorption of ethyl alcohol.

on adsorption was developed by Irving Langmuir, who pointed out that the surface atoms of crystals have unsatisfied valences and are capable of compound formation. This type of adsorption is known as *specific* or *activated,* or sometimes it is called *chemisorption.*

The choice of a suitable catalyst for a particular reaction still remains essentially a trial-and-error process. In its present state, the understanding of catalysis and of reaction mechanisms is far from complete. Much more information about intermediate states is still needed. This area of study therefore offers a great opportunity for discovery.

Bonds in Particular

5

The Weakest

WHEN ANY TWO particles—atoms or molecules—approach each other closely enough, a bond may always be formed, linking these particles together. This is rather obvious when there is a reaction between particles and such bonds as covalent, ionic, metallic or hydrogen bonds are formed. However, if none of these bonds can form—between rare gas atoms, for example—there is still a kind of bond that can always occur. This is known as a *Van der Waals bond*. Because such bonds are so very weak, they are evident only in the absence of stronger bonds.

If no bonding were possible between two atoms or molecules of a certain type, then these particles could only exist as a gas. The constituent particles of a liquid are bonded together in fairly large aggregates; in a solid, the bonding may be continuous from particle to particle. All forms of gaseous matter, however, can be liquefied. Furthermore, all gases can be adsorbed on any surface, and gases are soluble, at least to some extent, in any liquid. Both adsorption and solution are impossible without bond formation. Therefore, it is always likely that a bond may occur between atoms and molecules, regardless of whether these particles are alike or different.

Van der Waals bonds were discovered and named long before there was any plausible explanation for their existence. Basically, these bonds are no different from the stronger bonds, and their formation similarly involves the electrons and atomic nuclei. The attraction between two atoms that results in Van der Waals bonds is essentially due to electrostatic forces between the electrons of one atom and the nucleus of another.

What are the nature and the effects of Van der Waals bonds? To answer these questions, we will also consider specific instances where such bonds occur in gases, liquids, and solids. As examples of solids, we will use inclusion compounds, which are composed of two molecular components, one forming a structure that has spaces in which molecules of the other component are accommodated. The bonds between two such components can be only of the Van der Waals type.

THE NATURE OF VAN DER WAALS BONDS

First, let's visualize atoms and molecules as being composed of positively charged elements, the nuclei, surrounded by the negatively charged electrons, as discussed in detail in Chapter Two. An electron is at a relatively large distance from a nucleus. Van der Waals bonds are of significance for neutral atoms and molecules, whose total electronic charge is equal to the nuclear charge.

The arrangement of the electrons about the nucleus is important. They may be symmetrically distributed, as illustrated in Fig. 5.1. This electron arrangement is far from exact, but it serves to illustrate the idea. The electrons in a molecule may tend, on the other hand, to concentrate nearer one particular end of the molecule than the other. The molecule as a whole is neutral and may be described as shown in Fig. 5.2, with a net charge, $\delta-$, near one extremity balanced by a

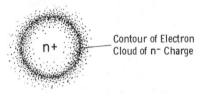

Contour of Electron
Cloud of n^- Charge

n+

Figure 5.1. A symmetric distribution of n electrons about a nucleus of n^+ charge.

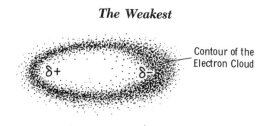

Figure 5.2. A dipolar molecule.

positive charge, $\delta+$, at the other. This is called a *polar molecule,* or it is said to possess a *dipole* in reference to its unsymmetrical distribution of positive and negative charges. The magnitude of these positive and negative charges, $\delta+$ and $\delta-$, is less than a single electronic charge. If an unsymmetrical distribution of electronic charge is an inherent property of a molecule, and if this distribution is not due to external effects, the molecule is known as a *permanent dipole.*

When a symmetrical molecule is completely isolated, it has no dipole. However, it may acquire one by the action of an external electric field, as illustrated in Fig. 5.3. In this figure, the molecule is located between a positive and a negative plate, and the electric field causes the electrons to shift so that there is a slight excess of $\delta-$ charge near the end closer to the positive pole, and a compensating $\delta+$ charge at the opposite end. This is known as an *induced dipole.* The $\delta-$ and $\delta+$ charges in one dipolar molecule create an electric

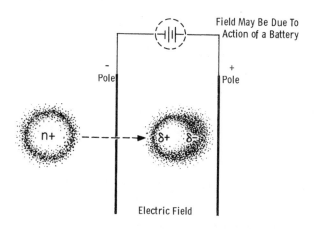

Figure 5.3. The effect of an electric field on a symmetrical atom.

field that may act on another molecule and thereby induce a dipole in it. It is essentially a case of electrons—in the molecule acquiring an induced dipole—being shifted as they are repelled or attracted by the $\delta-$ or the $\delta+$ charge on the other molecule.

We have already noted that Van der Waals bonds, or forces, result from electrostatic interactions. These electrostatic forces occur between either permanent dipole molecules or induced dipole molecules. Van der Waals bonds are formed by three mechanisms. For atoms or molecules with *no* permanent dipole, bonding occurs by the *dispersion effect*, the mechanism involving the formation of induced dipoles. When a molecule has permanent dipoles, bonding occurs by the *orientation effect* and the *induction effect*, as well as the dispersion effect.

Chronologically, the orientation effect, which pertains specifically to molecules with permanent dipoles, was the first mechanism suggested for Van der Waals bonds. In this effect, the positive portion of one molecule is electrostatically attracted to the negative part of another. This specific arrangement is preferred for two molecules that are near each other, rather than an arrangement in which the molecules are randomly located with respect to each other. Hence, it is obvious why this is called the orientation effect. Furthermore, aggregates of more than two molecules—either in long chains or in closed loops—may be formed by this effect, with successive molecules being attracted to one another through oppositely charged portions of their dipoles.

The induction effect is a more subtle mechanism. A molecule with a permanent dipole may induce an additional dipole in another molecule. When all the molecules are the same, this effect occurs mutually between any two molecules that are close to each other. What actually happens is that the positive portion of one molecule causes a shift of electrons to the already electron-rich part of the other molecule. This positive segment is neutralized, to some extent, by the close presence of the negative charge of the other molecule, and the neutralization is enhanced by the additional charge that is induced. Attraction between two unlike charges involves reduction, or neutralization, of the charge unbalance represented by each of them. Accordingly, the induction effect provides forces that bind two molecules together. It affords a means for attraction not only between two permanent dipoles, but also between one molecule with a large dipole and another with no dipole whatever.

The dispersion effect is not only present in the Van der Waals bonds involving permanent molecular dipoles, but it also accounts for the attraction between symmetrical molecules or atoms with no dipole. Total absence of a dipole in a molecule occurs only if there is no electric field acting on it. When two molecules with no permanent dipoles are close together, each exerts an electric field on the other. Even a molecule with no permanent dipole possesses an *oscillating dipole*, because of the oscillation of the electrons and atoms. Furthermore, at any particular time it may possess a dipole, even if *on the average* it has none. The electrons of one molecule repel those of the other when the two molecules are closest to each other. The dipole so induced in the second molecule will, in turn, induce a dipole in the first one, and therefore further attraction ensues between two mutually induced dipoles. This is a very simplified description of the dispersion effect, but it will serve our present purposes.

Now, as the separation distance between two molecules decreases, the Van der Waals forces of attraction between them increases. In other words, as the two molecules approach each other, their dipoles, either permanent or induced, become ever more prone to decrease the distance separating them. However, when the molecules are sufficiently close, the electrons surrounding one will repel the electrons about the other. This repulsive force prevents interpenetration of the two groups of electrons, and the repulsion increases with decreasing distance of separation. When the separation distance becomes small enough, this repulsive force is very much greater than the Van der Waals force of attraction. However, the two forces—repulsion and attraction—are always present, and it is the resulting *net* force that affects a pair of molecules. If the force of repulsion is numerically greater than that of attraction, the molecules tend to separate farther apart, but if the attractive force is greater, they will tend to be drawn closer together.

Let's consider the sequence of effects that occur when two molecules are separated farther and farther from each other. Hypothetically, they are so close to each other in the beginning that there would be interpenetration of their electrons. At first, the net force is one of repulsion. This effect decreases with increasing separation, because the repulsive force is diminished much more than the attractive force by a given increase in intermolecular separation. At a certain separation distance, the net force becomes zero; then, at greater separation distances, the forces of attraction predominate so that the net force is one of attraction. The separation distance at which the net force is zero is of the utmost significance. Here, the forces of attraction are equal to those of repulsion, and, consequently, these forces in no way influence the molecules either to move farther apart or to come closer together. This is the preferred distance of separation. At smaller separations, the molecules repel each other and move apart, and at greater distances, they move toward each other; in each case, the effect is to move the molecules to the preferred distance of separation where the net force is zero.

The interplay between these attractive and repulsive forces is illustrated in the potential energy diagram of Fig. 5.4. The potential energy between two particles is the negative of the energy of attraction between them. The energy of attraction here is the amount of work that has to be done to move the two particles far away from each other. The more negative the potential energy, the more work must be done to pull the particles apart. Two particles will behave in such a way that the potential energy between them is as low as possible. This occurs when the forces of repulsion and attraction cancel each other and their sum is zero. If the particles—molecules or atoms —are at a separation distance where the potential energy decreases with decreasing distance, they will be drawn even closer together. Conversely, if the potential energy increases with decreasing distance, the two particles will move apart. When the potential energy is the lowest one possible, no change occurs in the separation distance, since moving either way increases the potential energy.

To explain the potential energy curve in Fig. 5.4, we can say that in increasing any separation distance, work must be done *on* the molecules when the potential energy decreases with decreasing distance, but work is done *by* the molecules themselves when the potential energy increases with decreasing distance. The maximum amount of work is needed to separate the molecules far apart when they are at the distance *B* from each other, the minimum in the potential energy dia-

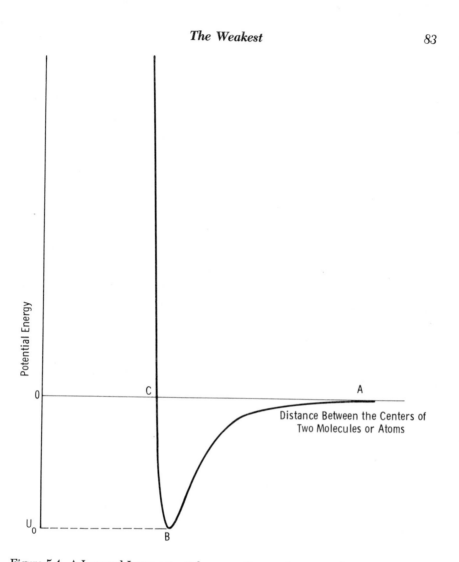

Figure 5.4. A Lennard-Jones potential energy diagram for two molecules at different separation distances. Van der Waals forces act between them.

gram. This work is equal in magnitude to the numerical value of U_0. Here the molecules are most stable with regard to the distance of separation. The distance B is essentially a trap for the two molecules and is at the bottom of what is known as a *potential well*.

At separations larger than B, the molecules are under the influence of a net attractive force, and the work required to move them far apart is less than that needed at the bottom of the potential well. Also for separation distances less than B, when the net force is one of repulsion, the work required to move the molecules far apart is less than if they are initially at B, because they will first reach B by doing work themselves. At C, the potential energy is zero, and no work is required to separate the molecules far apart, making the situation the same here as if they were far apart to begin with. Consequently, the separation C is the closest approach of two molecules for the condition of free collision, and is known as the *Van der Waals diameter*. The molecules could not come any closer than that, unless a strong bond is formed, because the potential energy is then positive and the molecules will do work themselves to separate.

The points we have made above apply to two isolated molecules or atoms. In general, however, the attractive forces occur between one molecule and *more* than one other neighboring molecule. With many molecules in a given volume, the Van der Waals energy of attraction, corresponding to U_0, is about 5 to 10 kcal/mole.

It is interesting to compare separation distances due to Van der Waals bonds with those due to strong chemical bonds. For example, let's consider graphite, which consists of carbon atoms. These carbon atoms are arranged in layers, as mentioned in Chapter One. There are covalent bonds between the atoms in a layer, and Van der Waals bonds between the layers themselves. The distance between neighboring carbon atoms in a layer is 1.42 Å, and the distance between closest carbon atoms in two successive layers is 3.40 Å. The chemical bond brings atoms or molecules closer together than the Van der Waals diameter, which is about 10 percent less than the Van der Waals bond. This is the closest approach possible when only Van der Waals forces are present.

There is no general theory to describe the relationship between potential energy and separation distance for any two molecules. This appears to be a problem of considerable magnitude. For many molecules, the potential energy of attraction only is found to be:

$$M/r^6,$$

where r is the separation distance and M is a constant. Certain theoretical calculations give the potential energy for repulsive effects only as:

$$N/r^{12},$$

where N is a constant that is related to M. The total potential energy is then:

$$U = N/r^{12} - M/r^6,$$

and this is negative for all separation distances above C in Fig. 5.4. At B in this figure, U is equal to U_0. This relationship is known as the *Lennard-Jones potential*, which is the curve in Fig. 5.4. Although it is based on numerous approximations, it has been found very useful.

Van der Waals bonds are often easily broken by the thermal energy of molecules. This energy is directly proportional to the temperature and is approximately equal to kT for a molecule, where k is Boltzmann's constant. It is manifest in the tendency of molecules or atoms to move about. Very few molecules in a gas are bound together by Van der Waals bonds; most of them move freely as individual particles. As the temperature is lowered, there is less and less opposition to their being bound by these bonds, and an increasing number of molecules are held together by Van der Waals bonds. These bonds form a continuous network throughout the solid whose molecules are held together by Van der Waals bonds.

VAN DER WAALS BONDS IN GASES

In the 1880's, the Dutch physicist Johannes Van der Waals presented the idea that weak bonds occur between gas molecules. He based his conclusion on the differences in pressure-volume relationships observed for gases at high pressures and those obtained at low pressures. Another phenomenon, called the *Joule-Thomson effect*, was also observed to result from Van der Waals bonds in gases. This effect is the decrease or the increase in the temperature of a gas that results when the gas is forced, under pressure, through an orifice or porous plug. The gas is caused to expand in volume as it goes from high to low pressure across the barrier. A decrease in temperature occurs when the gas initially, on the high pressure side, is below a certain critical temperature; above this temperature the Joule-Thomson effect is one that increases the gas temperature. To understand these phenomena, let's examine a few more details.

The pressure-volume relationship for a gas at low pressures, in the range of one atmosphere, is close to what is called an *ideal gas* behavior. This behavior would be expected if the molecules of the gas were not all attracted to each other and if the volume of the molecules themselves were negligible compared to that of the container. In theory, the product of the pressure and the volume of an ideal gas is constant at a given temperature, the relationship for one mole of gas being

$$PV = RT,$$

where P is the pressure, V is the volume, R is the gas constant, and T is the temperature. For every decrease in volume, a corresponding fractional increase in pressure occurs, and vice versa. At sufficiently high pressures or sufficiently low temperatures, this ideal behavior ceases to be true. A typical pressure-volume relationship at high pressures is given in Fig. 5.5. First, the pressure-volume product decreases, with increasing pressure, and then this product increases. The constant PV line is shown dashed in this figure, giving the "ideal" relationship. The decreasing and increasing PV behavior can be explained on the basis of the relationship between the forces of attraction and the separation distance, given in Fig. 5.4.

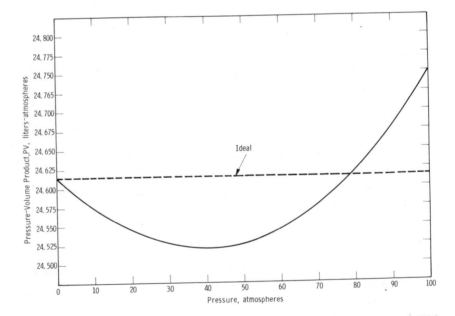

Figure 5.5. The pressure-volume relationship, PV versus P, for nitrogen gas at 27°C.

Pairs of molecules that are nearest neighbors in a gas are separated by distances ranging from very small to very large. As pressure increases, shorter separation distances are more and more predominant. At relatively low pressures, there are few pairs of molecules whose separations fall within the range of B in Fig. 5.4, where the Van der Waals forces of attraction are operative. Resistance to compression is rare here, since it calls for separation distances that are only of lower magnitude than B. Therefore, ideal gas behavior is observed, and PV is constant with pressure.

With increasing pressure, a departure from ideal gas conditions is observed when the Van der Waals forces of attraction affect a significant number of molecules in a gas. This happens as the distance between pairs of molecules diminishes and an appreciable fraction of all the molecules are separated from their nearest neighbors by distances where the potential energy decreases with decreasing distance. Since such molecules tend to be attracted to one another, they contribute less resistance to confinement than do the molecules that are not attracted to others. Therefore, the pressure is lower than that given by the ideal gas relation, $P = RT/V$. At these pressures, the number of neighboring molecules in the range of Van der Waals forces of attraction increases with increasing pressure. Small separations, rare at lower pressures, become more and more dominant with increasing pressures. Hence, the amount the pressure is diminished from its ideal value increases with increased pressure or with a decrease in the volume confining the gas. Van der Waals found that this decrement in pressure from the ideal value is equal to a/V^2, where a is a constant, characteristic of the gas, and V is the volume at that pressure. The initial part of the curve in Fig. 5.5, where PV decreases with pressure, is represented by the equation in the following forms:

$$(P + a/V^2)V = RT,$$
$$PV = RT - a/V,$$
and
$$P = RT/V - a/V^2.$$

Now let's consider the portion of the curve at very high pressures, where PV increases with pressure. At these pressures, an appreciable number of pairs of molecules have separation distances below B in Fig. 5.4. Under these conditions, the molecules in these pairs repel each other. Therefore, the pressure can be above the ideal gas pressure, provided the number of molecules involved with repulsive forces exceeds the number of those affected by attraction forces. This is the case above 40 to 50 atmospheres in Fig. 5.5. The repulsion is associated with the volume of the molecules themselves, or the space they occupy with respect to the volume of gas. In a given volume, there is less repulsion between small molecules than between relatively large ones. The pressure-volume relationship here, for one mole of gas, is:

$$P(V - b) = RT, \qquad P = RT/(V - b),$$

where b turns out to be four times the volume of the gas molecules themselves.

The equation corresponding to the pressure region, where only attractive forces between molecules predominate, and the one which considers only repulsive forces, can be combined into one equation that applies essentially to all pressures. This is the famous *Van der Waals equation:*

$$(P + a/V^2)(V - b) = RT.$$

Starting from low pressure, V is so large relative to a and b that the a/V^2 and b terms can be neglected, and the ideal gas assumption is valid. Then, with increasing pressures, only the effect of attraction predominates. The full equation applies principally to the region where both attractive and repulsive forces are effective. At very high pressures, repulsion between molecules outweighs any effects of attraction between them. It should be pointed out that the Van der Waals equation describes pressure-volume relations only approximately. However, it is very useful and quite valid, as such, and because other properties of the gas molecules can be fairly well predicted from it.

Now let's get back to the Joule-Thomson effect mentioned earlier, regarding the increase or decrease in the temperature of a gas when it goes from high to low pressure across a constriction. The procedure used here is one of several possible ways to change the volume of a gas *adiabatically*. An *adiabatic* change refers to a physical occurrence in which heat is neither added to nor removed from the entire system involved. For this purpose, the system has to be thermally insulated from its surroundings. One adiabatic change in volume of a gas is caused by having the gas do work to make it expand, or having work done on the gas to compress it. Here, an ideal gas would decrease in temperature on expanding and increase in temperature on being compressed. (The latter is the manner in which air is caused to ignite diesel fuel, when the piston compresses the air and a high temperature is obtained.) A gas can be made to change volume without its doing any work at all or having any work done on it. The simplest way to do this is by the *Joule method*, whereby a gas is expanded into an evacuated vessel from one that is pressurized. Theoretically, an ideal gas would not change in temperature in this case. However, the Joule method is not amenable to precise experimental test, because even the very best thermal insulation greatly diminishes the temperature effects on a gas under these conditions. In the Joule-Thomson experiment, however, which is a modification of the Joule experiment, a steady stream of gas is maintained, going from high to low pressure. Under these conditions, an ideal gas would also not change in temperature. From an experimental point of view, the Joule-Thomson temperature effect is quite significant, since the effects occurring in the gas are not masked by the presence of the vessel through which the gas passes. This effect can be explained in a manner similar to the explanation given for the decreasing portion of the *PV* curve in Fig. 5.5. On the high-pressure side of the orifice, an appreciable number of molecules are affected by Van der Waals forces of attraction, and a relatively small number undergo repulsion from one another. When this gas changes from high to low pressure, it becomes more like an ideal gas. Molecules are freed from attractive forces, because fewer have intermolecular distances in the range of attraction. To remove the forces of attraction from some of the molecules during decompression, energy has to be supplied to them; in the Joule-Thomson effect, this energy is obtained from the thermal energy contained in all the molecules in the gas. Loss of thermal energy is manifested by a decrease in temperature. Therefore, in using thermal energy to overcome Van der Waals forces of attraction, the temperature is effectively decreased on the high-pressure side.

At a sufficiently high temperature, decompression of a gas produces an increase in temperature. The energy obtained from the repulsive part of the Van der Waals force, which may be greater than the attraction effect at high temperatures, is relaxed on decompression and increases the thermal energy of the gas.

VAN DER WAALS BONDS IN LIQUIDS

The Van der Waals forces that act between molecules of a gas can cause them to agglomerate as a liquid. In such a case, the Van der Waals equation obtained for the gas is applicable to the corresponding liquid. The a/V^2 term is especially significant and is known as the *internal pressure*, with V equal to the volume of one mole of liquid. The internal pressure is essentially related to the cohesion between the molecules of a liquid, and is comparable to the external pressure associated with the opposition of free gas molecules to their confining volume. The product of a/V^2 and V, a/V, is equal to the energy released when free gas molecules combine by Van der Waals bonding into agglomerates to form a liquid. (Note: (pressure) $\times$ (volume change against the pressure) = work done.) This is the *energy of liquefaction* of a gas, and the measured value, obtained by calorimetric methods, often agrees quite closely with the empirical a/V from the Van der Waals gas equation.

These similarities between a gas and a liquid do not apply when molecules are agglomerated as a liquid by other bonds in addition to Van der Waals bonds. In liquid water, for example, hydrogen bonds provide most of the attractive forces between the molecules, rather than the Van der Waals bonds present in the gas. In general, departures from gas-liquid similarities occur only with molecules having large permanent dipoles.

SOLUBILITY OF GASES IN LIQUIDS

The two components in a solution are called the *solute* and the *solvent*, and the solute is dissolved by the solvent. Solubility is often expressed as the mole fraction of the solute, that is, as the ratio of the number of moles of solute to the total number of moles in solution:

$$\text{mole fraction}_{\text{solute}} = X_{\text{solute}} = \frac{\text{moles solute}}{\text{moles solute} + \text{moles solvent}},$$

and

$$X_{\text{solute}} + X_{\text{solvent}} = 1.$$

When the solubility is very low, there being many more molecules of solvent than solute, each solute molecule may be surrounded by only solvent molecules and relatively far from other solute molecules. This situation of the dilute solution is best understood by first considering the properties of solutions.

The solubility of a solute in a solvent is generally related to *Henry's law*, which states that the solubility of a given solute, in mole fraction, is equal to the ratio of its vapor pressure above the solution to the vapor pressure of only condensed solute molecules. Thus,

$$X_{\text{solute}} = \frac{P_{\text{solute}}}{P^{\circ}_{\text{solute}}}. \tag{5.1}$$

A solute and a solution containing such solute molecules is illustrated in Fig. 5.6. Henry's law applies well to solutions whose solute and solvent molecules interact with their own kind and with each other only by Van der Waals bonds. The vapor pressure, $P^{\circ}_{\text{solute}}$, of the solute is related to the internal pressure of the solute molecules, which

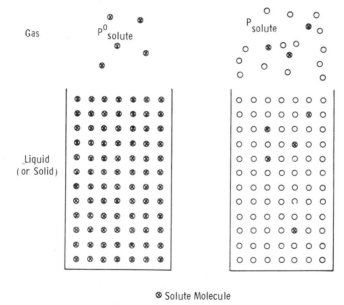

⊗ Solute Molecule

○ Solvent Molecule

Figure 5.6. Illustration of the vapor pressures of a pure liquid solute, and these molecules in a solvent.

they must overcome in the liquid in order to escape as gaseous molecules. The greater the *cohesiveness* between molecules in the liquid or, equivalently, the greater the internal pressure, the less the tendency to evaporate or the less the vapor pressure. In the pure solute, all molecules in the liquid contribute to the vapor pressure. When solute molecules are present in a solution and the neighboring solvent molecules also have the same internal pressure, each solute molecule behaves very much as it does when it has only its own kind surrounding it. Van der Waals bonds of the same magnitude are also established between the solute and the solvent molecules. Each solute molecule in the solution will similarly contribute to the solute vapor pressure, just as those in the pure solute do. The total vapor pressure of the solute in the solution, therefore, is equal to the product of the mole fraction of the solute, X_{solute}, and the vapor pressure of the pure solute, $P°_{solute}$. When X_{solute} is equal to one, there are only solute molecules, and P_{solute} is equal to $P°_{solute}$.

A negative deviation from Henry's law occurs when the solubility, X_{solute}, is lower than that given by Eq. 5.1. In effect, a certain pressure of solute gas above a solvent liquid does not produce a solubility, according to Henry's law. This deviation occurs for solutions where all intermolecular interactions are of the Van der Waals type, but the internal pressures, or cohesiveness, of the solute and of the solvent are different. If the internal pressure of the solute is greater than that of the solvent, solute molecules would not be as attracted to the solution as to the pure solute. On the other hand, a greater cohesiveness between solvent molecules than between solute molecules would result in the solvent molecules tending to be associated with each other in the solution, rather than associating with solute molecules. In either case, the preference for one of the components of the solution to assume the pure form causes the solubility to be relatively lower than it would be if Henry's law were obeyed.

When the solute and the solvent form a compound, positive deviations from Henry's law are observed. That is, the solubility is greater than that predicted by Eq. 5.1. Henry's law is related to the weak Van der Waals bonds associated with the liquefaction of many gases. Where solute molecules react with a solvent to form a compound which has stronger bonds than those between the solute molecules and those between the solvent molecules, a greater amount of solute will be dissolved than is predicted by Henry's law.

SOLID INCLUSION COMPOUNDS

Just as Van der Waals forces may provide the cohesion between molecules of a liquid, and between a liquid and a second component dissolved in it, so these forces also appear in solids. In a crystal of solid material whose bonding is of the Van der Waals type, all of the molecules are interconnected by these bonds, as previously discussed in more detail in Chapter Three. There are solid solutions in which solute atoms or molecules are bonded to a solid. An *inclusion compound* is such a solid whose second component, or solute, is bound to the solid structure by Van der Waals forces.

The simplest case where this happens is in the adsorption of a single layer of atoms or molecules on the surface of a solid. The Van der Waals bonds, extending from the surface of the solid, cannot include more than one layer of adsorbed molecules. This can be seen from the potential energy diagram shown in Fig. 5.4, where the attractive forces are very small at two atomic or molecular distances between two particles; that is, at $2 \times A$. In many ways, an inclusion compound is similar to a solid with a single layer of adsorbed molecules. They may be considered analogous in terms of adsorption, but an inclusion compound contains molecules that are adsorbed on a surface in a rather complicated manner compared to simple adsorption.

The component that provides the solid structure in an inclusion compound is called the *host*. The host contains spaces or locations in which the molecules or atoms of the other component, called the *guest*, are located. These spaces have their own specific structure which depends on the host. Therefore, a given host may accommodate only those guest molecules that can be suitably located in the spaces it provides. An inclusion compound cannot be formed between a host and guest molecules that are too large to fit in the available spaces, for example. In ordinary chemical reactions where strong bonds are made, the geometry and size of the reacting molecules are generally of secondary importance.

There are three kinds of inclusion compounds, and each is related to a specific type of space provided by the host for guest molecules. In certain inclusion compounds, the host molecules are arranged in layers, and the spaces between these layers can be occupied by guest molecules. These are called *layer compounds*. In those called *channel compounds*, the host contains long channel-like spaces in which guest molecules can be located. This structure, in its simplest form, may resemble a honeycomb or a neatly piled stack of pipes. Certain other host compounds assume a structure containing completely enclosed cages. Guest molecules must be of a suitable size to fit in these cages, and certain cages may accommodate more than one molecule. The cage isolates the molecule contained in it, and there is no ready escape for such a guest from this *clathrate*, as there is from the other two inclusion compounds. (See examples in Fig. 5.7.)

Graphite and mica are examples of layer compounds. The carbon atoms in graphite are arranged in layers composed of continuous hexagonal patterns, with each atom common to three hexagons, as shown in Fig. 1.1. The structure of a specific mica (there are various kinds) is essentially an alumino silicon oxide with alkali ions, and it is much more complicated than the structure of graphite. In both graphite and mica, guest molecules, ranging in size from water molecules to hydrocarbons and their derivatives, can be located between layers. There are many combinations of alumino silicon oxides and suitable cations, whose structures include extensive arrangements of channel-like cavities. These host materials are found among natural

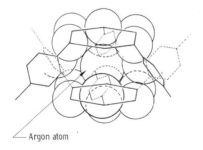

(a) Argon Clathrate of Hydroquinone

Argon atom

(Courtesy of H. M. Powell.)

Figure 5.7a. Argon atom at center; other atoms are from surrounding hydroquinone molecules; front atoms are omitted from the structure so that argon is visible. Circles denote all the space occupied by the atoms.

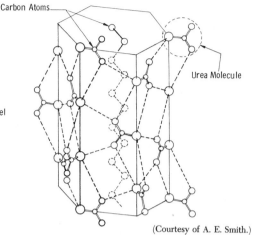

Carbon Atoms

Urea Molecule

(b) Hydrocarbon Molecule in Urea Channel

(Courtesy of A. E. Smith.)

Figure 5.7b. Carbon atoms from included hydrocarbon molecule; other atoms are urea molecules located about the hexagonal structure. Circles denote positions of the atoms.

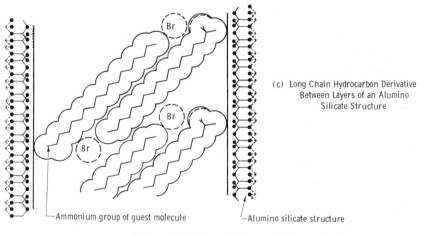

Br

Br

Br

(c) Long Chain Hydrocarbon Derivative Between Layers of an Alumino Silicate Structure

—Ammonium group of guest molecule

—Alumino silicate structure

(Courtesy of Clay Minerals Bulletin, Blackwell Scientific Publications, Ltd.)

Figure 5.7c. Cross-sectional view, showing that the guest molecules are tilted between the host layers.

minerals which are called *zeolites*, and are known as *molecular sieves* when synthesized artificially. Such a structure has certain character-istic channel dimensions, and these vary from one to another, so that a large number of molecules of different sizes may be guests in suitably specific channel structures. Molecules of the size of H_2O, He, and N_2, and those smaller than CH_4 and Kr, can be included in molecular sieves with the smallest channels available at present. Much larger molecules, of the size of 1,3,5-triethyl benzene, are about the largest that can be accommodated in the largest channels that have so far been obtained in a sieve type. Urea forms hexagonal channels about straight chain hydrocarbon molecules (Fig. 5.7) and likewise thiourea is the host in inclusion compounds with bulky hydrocarbon molecules, such as branched chains (5.A) or chains of benzene rings. Hydroquinone

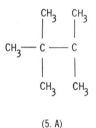

(5. A)

forms clathrate compounds with molecules like CH_3OH, Ar, SO_2, Cl_2, and HCl as guest compounds. It is worth noting that a rare gas such as argon can be retained in these clathrate cavities and is readily released only if the structure of the hydroquinone is broken by melting or by dissolution. Water assumes a clathrate structure with suitable guest molecules. There are two types of water clathrates, and the cages in each type are of two different sizes. One kind of water clathrate forms double clathrates containing two different types of guest molecules. The large cavities accommodate the larger molecules, and the smaller molecules are located in the small cavities.

Layer structures are fairly flexible, and the distance between layers in a layer inclusion compound is partially determined by the size of the guest molecules. It has been found that a layer host structure will *swell* when guest molecules are being incorporated into it, or when large guest molecules replace small ones. On the other hand, channel and clathrate structures are comparatively fixed. But in all cases, it is the Van der Waals dimension of a molecule that determines whether it has the correct geometry and size to be included in such structures.

Although the bonds between host and guest molecules in an inclusion compound are of the Van der Waals type, the bonds between the host molecules are usually of stronger kinds. Guest molecules are often separated from each other by intervening host molecules. If they are close to one another, the guest-to-guest bonds between adjacent molecules are the same as in the pure compound. Because of the weak host-to-guest interactions, the components in an inclusion compound show many of the same properties they exhibit when they are separate.

It is impossible to form an inclusion compound between a host and a guest, even of suitable size, if bonding between the two is stronger than the Van der Waals kind. When there is an appreciably strong bond between two such components, it becomes an integral part of the solid structure. The structure is intimately related to this bond and it is no longer that of the host type, being instead that of a specific compound composed of two molecular components, strongly bound to each other.

Some host materials cannot assume a host structure unless a certain fraction of the spaces in the inclusion compound is occupied by guest molecules. Even if the presence of guests is necessary for the formation of the host structure, the essential structure of the solid is provided only by the host.

Ever since the pioneer work of Van der Waals himself in the 1880's, the study of Van der Waals forces has proved fascinating and has attracted the interest of many scientists. The practical and theoretical applications of these phenomena and related ideas are many and varied. Molecular and atomic dimensions can be determined from pressure-volume data. The cooling in the Joule-Thomson effect is used in a process called *gas liquefaction,* which involves pressurizing and cooling the gas. Vapor pressures and solubilities of solute gases in liquids can be estimated. The theory affords an experimental method of determining the nature of solutes in solvents. Inclusion compounds, particularly of the channel type, are used to separate mixtures of different molecules. Here, one host structure will selectively form an inclusion compound with one type of molecule as defined by its size and shape. An interesting use of clathrates has been in studying the behavior of individual molecules when, as guests, they are completely isolated by the cage structure.

6

Unfamiliar
Bonds

FEW RECENT DEVELOPMENTS in chemistry have created more interest than the discovery that the noble gases can be induced to enter into chemical combinations with other elements.

As early as 1785, the English chemist Henry Cavendish found that although most of the air in a closed vessel could be removed by chemical methods, about one percent, by volume, always remained unreacted. But a century was to pass before this small component of air was recognized as a new element. Toward the end of the nineteenth century, the physicist Lord Rayleigh noted that the density of nitrogen prepared from air (by the removal of oxygen) was always greater than that prepared from other sources, such as ammonia. This suggested that nitrogen prepared from air was actually a mixture containing a small amount of an unknown element or compound, in addition to nitrogen. The chemist William Ramsay took up the problem, and he was able to remove the nitrogen by adsorbing it on hot magnesium metal. Rayleigh and Ramsay eventually collaborated, and after much hard work they were able to show that they had a new gaseous element, which they called *argon*. The most interesting characteristic of the new gas was its chemical inertness. No reaction could be obtained with any of a wide variety of reagents. It was prophetic, however, that these two investigators suggested that a reaction might be obtained with fluorine.

Publication of these results in 1895 created great interest and much controversy, especially since there seemed no place to fit the new element into the accepted periodic table of the time. With Ramsay's subsequent discovery of the additional inert gases helium, neon, krypton, xenon, and radon in the years from 1895 to 1900, there came the realization that these gases belonged as a group in a separate column of the periodic table.

The chemical inertness of these noble gases has seemed so well established that there have been few serious attempts in recent years to make them undergo chemical reaction. Reaction was finally achieved only very recently by a rather indirect series of events. As part of a series of experiments at the University of British Columbia, Neil Bartlett and D. H. Lohmann were able to react molecular oxygen and PtF_6 in a one-to-one molecular ratio to obtain interesting ionic compound $O_2^+(PtF_6)^-$. The production of this compound involves the removal of an electron from O_2. A measure of the energy required to remove an electron from a molecule or atom is the *ionization potential*. Bartlett noted a close similarity between the ionization potentials of O_2 (12.2 electron volts) and the noble gas xenon (12.1 electron volts), which suggested to him that xenon might form a similar compound with PtF_6. When Bartlett mixed gaseous PtF_6 with xenon gas, he did indeed obtain a yellow powder to which he assigned the structure $Xe^+(PtF_6)^-$, on the basis of further studies. (It is now known that the reaction is actually somewhat more complicated, giving compounds of composition $Xe(PtF_6)_x$, where x can vary from 1 to 2.)

When this work was published in 1962, it created great interest, and investigations on xenon chemistry were taken up at other laboratories. At the Argonne National Laboratory, H. Classen, H. Selig, and J. C. Malm were able to obtain reaction between the elements xenon and fluorine by heating them together in a nickel can. The result was a white crystalline material which proved to be XeF_4. Additional work at Argonne and elsewhere soon showed that other fluorides, XeF_2, and XeF_6, could also be prepared by varying the experimental conditions.

The results obtained with xenon have prompted workers to attempt also the preparation of fluorides from the other noble gases. Radon has a lower ionization potential than xenon does, and hence would be expected to react with fluorine. Work with trace amounts of radon indicates that fluorides, in fact, do form, but the highly radioactive nature of radon has prevented obtaining such compounds in quantity. However, the compounds KrF_2 and KrF_4 have been obtained in substantial amounts from krypton. To date, there has been no success in preparing fluorides from helium, neon, or argon. With these elements, the high ionization potentials may make any latent compounds too unstable to be isolated. With the exceptions we have mentioned, the chemistry of the noble gases is largely restricted, at the moment, to the chemistry of xenon.

Using the xenon fluorides as starting materials, further chemical reactions are possible to give additional xenon compounds; over twenty such compounds have been prepared to date. The reactions that have been achieved are summarized in Fig. 6.1.

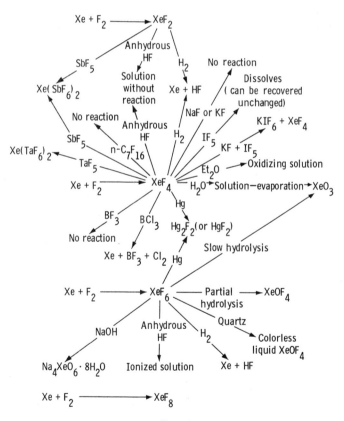

(From *Progress in Inorganic Chemistry*, Vol. 6. New York: Interscience Publishers, Inc., 1964. Adapted and redrawn.)

Figure 6.1. Reactions of xenon fluorides.

Much of the current interest in xenon compounds centers on their structures and mode of bonding, and more progress has been made in understanding the former than the latter. Discovery of the noble gas compounds at this late date has benefited from the availability of sophisticated methods of structural investigation, which were not available a few years ago. As a result of the intense effort devoted to the noble gas compounds in the last three years, more is now known about them than about many less exotic substances.

The most direct and unambiguous method of studying structure in solid crystalline compounds is by diffraction techniques, which will be discussed in detail in Chapter Eight. Several xenon compounds have now been investigated by either x-ray or neutron diffraction, or both. The molecular structure of XeF_4 is shown in Fig. 6.2, as deduced by x-ray diffraction. The four fluorines and the xenon atom all lie in a plane. The way these molecules are arranged relative to each other in the crystal is shown in Fig. 6.3. The three atoms are colinear in XeF_2 (Fig. 6.4), while the arrangement of atoms in XeO_3 is that shown in Fig. 6.5.

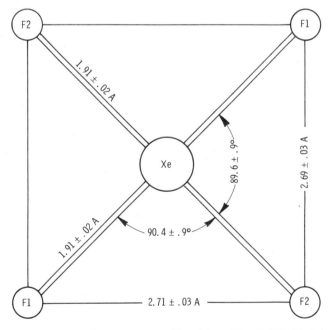

(From *Science*, *139*, 107; 1963. Adapted and redrawn.)

Figure 6.2. Molecular dimensions in XeF_4.

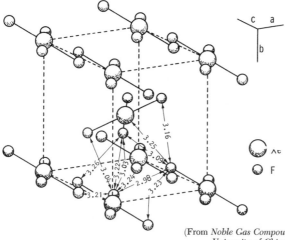

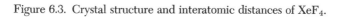

(From *Noble Gas Compounds*, H. H. Hyman, editor.
University of Chicago Press, 1963. Redrawn.)

Figure 6.3. Crystal structure and interatomic distances of XeF₄.

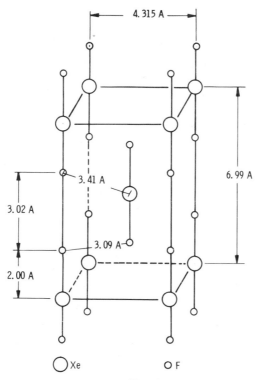

(From *Science, 139,* 843; 1963. Adapted and redrawn.)

Figure 6.4. Crystal structure and interatomic distances of XeF₂.

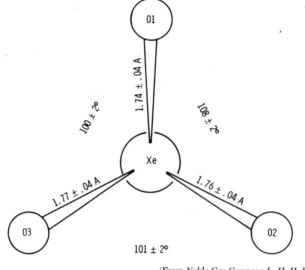

(From *Noble Gas Compounds*, H. H. Hyman, editor.
University of Chicago Press, 1963. Redrawn.)

Figure 6.5. Molecular dimensions of XeO_3.

Infrared absorption spectra, together with the related technique of Raman spectroscopy, have proved valuable tools in the study of the xenon fluorides. The observed spectra for some of the compounds are sufficiently simple that the peaks observed can be assigned to specific molecular vibrations, and the geometry and symmetry of the molecules can be determined unambiguously. The geometries deduced in this manner agree with those determined by x-ray and neutron diffraction. Fig. 6.6 shows the observed wavenumber values, together with molecular vibrations, for XeF_4 and $XeOF_4$.

Other techniques that have been used in the study of xenon compounds include Mössbauer spectra, nuclear magnetic resonance, and thermochemical investigations. (See Chapter Eight.) With respect to the last one, the heat effects accompanying reactions 6.1 and 6.2 have been measured. From the results, the xenon-fluorine bond energy in XeF_4 has been found to be about 30 kcal. This value is well within the range typical of more conventional chemical bonds.

$$XeF_4 + 4I^- \rightarrow 2I_2 + Xe + 4F^- \tag{6.1}$$

$$XeF_4 + 2H_2 \rightarrow Xe + 4HF \tag{6.2}$$

The nature of the bonding in xenon compounds is still a matter of much controversy. A number of theoretical treatments of varying degrees of sophistication have been advanced. Discussion has centered on whether the bonds are ionic or covalent (or have both ionic and covalent character) and, if covalent, how the electrons are distributed among available orbitals.

On the basis of available evidence, it is now rather generally agreed that the bonds in xenon compounds cannot be purely ionic. A treatment of bonding in these compounds, which is undoubtedly oversimplified but has predictive value, is based on covalent electron-pair bonding and the repulsion of an electron pair for other electron pairs.

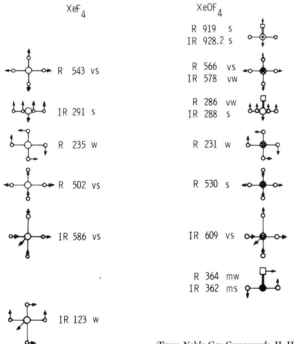

(From *Noble Gas Compounds*, H. H. Hyman, editor. University of Chicago Press, 1963. Redrawn.)

Figure 6.6. Vibrational modes and assignments for XeF_4 and $XeOF_4$. R = Raman spectrum; IR = infrared; s = strong; w = weak; m = medium; v = very. Numbers are in cm^{-1}.

(See Chapter Two.) Thus, in XeF_2, the Xe—F bonds are each made up of one of the eight valence electrons of Xe and an electron donated by the fluorine. The remaining six valence electrons of xenon are grouped into three pairs. The theory predicts that the two fluorine atoms and the remaining three lone pairs of electrons will take up positions about the xenon atom such as to minimize mutual repulsions. For XeF_2, this requires a linear arrangement of the three atoms, and this is what has been observed experimentally. Similarly, the XeF_4 should be planar, in agreement with experiment. While in the simplest arrangement for XeF_6 the fluorine atoms would be at the corners of a regular octahedron, the present theory predicts a nonoctahedral structure, since one lone pair of electrons will remain to distort the fluorines from the regular octahedral configuration. Very recently, workers at Iowa State University have shown by means of electron diffraction measurements that XeF_6 is indeed distorted from a regular octahedron.

More elaborate theoretical treatments of bonding in noble gas compounds have also been made in terms of *molecular orbital (M.O.)* theory. In general, M.O. theory requires the same molecular configurations as the simple repulsion theory we have just discussed. However, in the case of XeF_6, the M.O. treatment predicts a regular octahedral configuration of fluorine atoms about the Xe which, as indicated above, is not in accord with experimental observation.

BONDS IMPOSED BY GEOMETRY

The innumerable chemical compounds that form the subject matter of organic chemistry, both in the biological world and in the laboratory, owe their richness and diversity to the unique tendency of the element carbon to combine with itself or with other elements to form *linear* or *ring* molecules. Let's consider now some very unusual structures that can result from such ring formation.

From a consideration of molecular models, it has been known for some time that a ring of carbon atoms containing twenty or more members should have enough space in its center to allow a second ring to pass through, forming a two-link chain. The two rings in such an entity are not bonded to each other in the usual sense; nevertheless, they are inseparable, short of breaking one of the bonds in the two rings. Compounds made up of such double molecules would be expected to display interesting and subtle differences in properties, not found in the components when present as single rings.

Although some workers had postulated the existence of interlocking rings as part of the molecular structure of certain polymers, no evidence for definite interlocking ring compounds was obtained before 1960. In that year, H. L. Frisch and E. Wasserman of the Bell Telephone Laboratories were able to demonstrate interlocking ring formation in the manner shown in 6.A and 6.B.

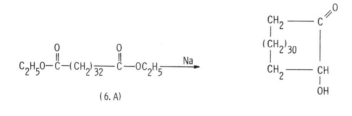

(6. A)

(6. B)

The long chain organic compound, designated 6.A (a diester), in the presence of sodium metal, undergoes the reaction shown to give the ring compound 6.B (called a *cyclic acyloin* by organic chemists). When this reaction was carried out in the presence of the cyclic hydrocarbon (6.C), a small amount of the acyloin 6.B produced was found to be linked inseparably with the hydrocarbon 6.C. This was

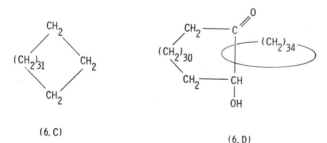

(6. C)

(6. D)

interpreted to mean that some of the compound 6.D, called generically a *catenane*, was produced. The species 6.D could not be separated from the larger amount of 6.B produced, but its presence was proved by using 6.C, in which some of the hydrogen atoms were replaced by heavy hydrogen (deuterium). The mixture containing 6.B and 6.D was shown by infrared absorption spectroscopy to contain deuterium. This could only mean that some of the hydrocarbon 6.C was linked in some fashion to the acyloin (6.B), since free hydrocarbon (6.C) was readily removed by chromatography.

The amount of catenane (6.D) produced in this experiment was only about one percent of the amount of free 6.B produced. This illustrates one of the principal difficulties in this type of work: the amount of product is dictated by statistical considerations. In order for the species 6.D to be produced, a molecule of 6.A must somehow thread its way through the center of the ring of the hydrocarbon 6.C and be in this position when the reaction (6.A and 6.B) occurs. This is a highly improbable series of events. If large amounts of compounds such as 6.D are to be produced, the chemist must find means for circumventing these unfavorable statistics. We should emphasize that the difficulty in making such materials in no way reflects on their stability once they are formed. There is no reason why a species such as 6.D should not be as stable as its separated components.

Two interlocking rings represent only the simplest case of many exotic configurations which are possible in principle. A theoretical consideration of what should be possible has intrigued chemists, although the practical considerations of actually synthesizing such species become enormously difficult as the complexity of the structures increases. The term "chemical topology" has been coined by Frisch and Wasserman to describe this area of study. Some of the configurations they have considered are shown in 6.E through 6.K.

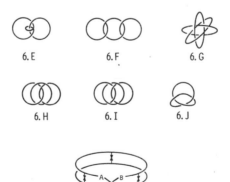

6. E   6. F   6. G

6. H   6. I   6. J

6. K

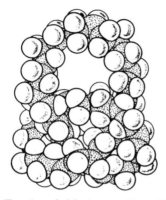

(From *Journal of the American Chemical Society, 83,* 3789; 1961. Redrawn.)

Figure 6.7. Model of a C_{54} trefoil hydrocarbon.

If both rings of atoms contain 33 members or more, a doubly wound ring (6.E) is possible. Three rings can be linked together in any of the four ways: 6.F, 6.G, 6.H, or 6.I. (Structure 6.G may be recognized as the trademark of P. Ballantine and Sons.) A single ring containing about 50 atoms can exist as a knot, or trefoil, form 6.J. An atom model of a $C_{54}H_{108}$ trefoil hydrocarbon is illustrated in Fig. 6.7.

Configuration 6.K, known as a *Moebius strip,* is a most interesting and intriguing one. This configuration and some of its unique properties can be illustrated with no more complicated equipment than a strip of paper, some transparent tape, and a pair of scissors. If the paper is given a half-twist along its long axis and the ends are joined with glue or tape, a Moebius strip results. This geometrical figure has only one surface and one edge, as can readily be seen by running a pencil along the surface or the edge. When the strip is cut in half, parallel to the edge, a single ring results. If instead, however, the cut is made one-third of the width from the edge (still parallel to the edge), two interlocking rings are formed. This is an entertaining parlor trick, which will confound most people. These properties have more serious implications, however, in that interlocking ring compounds might be made in this way, without the statistical limitations mentioned previously. We leave to the synthetic organic chemists the unsolved problems of how to do this on the molecular scale!

At present, the configurations we have discussed here are of more

interest theoretically than practically in that, except for the one example described, they have not actually been prepared in the laboratory. There is every reason to suppose, however, that synthetic
methods will eventually be found and that one day this may be an
active area of experimental investigation.

SANDWICH COMPOUNDS

Many discoveries in science have been made by accident, in the
course of searching for something quite different. One of the more
interesting recent examples is the discovery of the unusual iron compound *ferrocene*. In 1951, T. J. Kealy and P. L. Pauson, of Duquesne
University in Pittsburgh, reported an attempt to prepare the unknown
hydrocarbon *fulvalene* by means of the reaction 6.L. They obtained,
instead, an orange solid containing iron; after elemental analysis, this
could be written as $FeC_{10}H_{10}$.

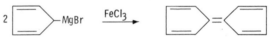

(6. L)

Almost at the same time—and quite independently—the English
workers Miller, Tebboth, and Tremaine reported the preparation of a
compound having the same formula, which they obtained by the
reaction of cyclopentadiene vapor, 6.M, with iron metal at 300°C.

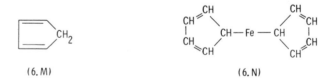

(6. M)   (6. N)

Both the English and the American workers named the compound
"dicyclopentadienyl iron" (the more convenient name ferrocene was
later coined by Woodward), and suggested 6.N as the structural formula for the compound. This compound was found to be soluble in
organic liquids and also remarkably stable to acids, bases, and heat.
The preparation of a compound such as 6.N created great interest almost
immediately, since no stable compound containing only carbon, hydro-

gen, and iron had previously been prepared. It soon became apparent that formula 6.N, in which iron is bonded to one specific carbon of each ring, could not account for the unusual physical and chemical properties of ferrocene. Since its discovery, the ensuing controversy over the true structure of ferrocene (and related compounds) has resulted in the publication of a great many scientific papers. The structure of ferrocene is now fairly well understood, as the result of using a variety of chemical and physical methods, although it must be admitted that there is still disagreement concerning the finer details of the bonding. The manner in which these various methods have been used to work out the structure of ferrocene is an interesting story and aptly illustrates how such procedures complement each other. Many of the methods used are of quite recent origin and would not have been available, say, twenty-five years ago.

About a year after the discovery of ferrocene, a group from Harvard University published their work with this compound. Their significant findings were these: (1) The infrared absorption spectrum of ferrocene in the region 3μ to 4μ contains only a single peak, which indicates that only one type of C—H bond is present. This is strong evidence against the structure 6.N, since the C—H bonds of the carbons attached directly to the iron should show different absorption frequencies from those of the other C—H bonds. (2) The electric dipole moment of the compound is zero, indicating a symmetrical structure about the iron. (3) The compound is diamagnetic. Hence, there are no unpaired electrons in the molecule.

On the basis of their findings, the Harvard group proposed unprecedented structures of the type 6.O or 6.P for ferrocene. In these structures,

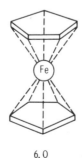

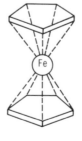

6. O   6. P

the iron is shown as bonding simultaneously to all ten carbon atoms. Structures in which the metal atom is held between planes formed by rings of carbon atoms have since come to be known by the descriptive term *sandwich* molecules.

The essential correctness of the sandwich structure was soon confirmed quite unambiguously by single crystal x-ray diffraction studies, carried out in several different laboratories. (See Chapter Eight.) In the crystal, ferrocene is held in the "staggered" configuration of 6.O, rather than the "eclipsed" structure 6.P. It was also found possible to study the compound in the vapor state (at the very high temperature of 400°C, in order to get sufficient vapor pressure) by the electron diffraction technique. These studies further confirmed the sandwich structure. However, in the vapor state, the two rings are free to rotate with respect to each other, which is also true in solution.

The precise mode of bonding in ferrocene is still a matter of some dispute. Early workers noted that the iron atom could attain the stable 18-electron configuration of the inert gas krypton (see Chapter Two), if it accepts all of the π-electrons of both rings into its vacant $3d$, $4s$, and $4p$ orbitals. The German chemist E. O. Fischer, who has made very significant contributions in this area of chemistry, holds strongly to this view, and draws the structure as 6.Q. On the other hand, the American

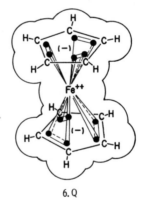

6.Q

workers G. Wilkinson and F. A. Cotton have argued, rather convincingly, that the complete donation of π-electrons from the rings to the iron atom, as in 6.Q, is too extreme a view. Wilkinson and Cotton hold that, while some donation of π-electrons to iron undoubtedly takes place, this donation cannot be considered complete and that significant π-

electron density must remain on the rings. A number of different workers have treated the bonding in ferrocene by molecular orbital theory. Such treatments always involve certain assumptions, however, whose accuracy is difficult to assess on the basis of present knowledge.

ORGANIC DERIVATIVES OF FERROCENE

Each of the organic rings of ferrocene contains five bonded hydrogen atoms. (See 6.Q.) At least in principle, any or all of these 10 hydrogen atoms could be replaced by other atoms or groupings, such as Cl, Br, CH_3, COOH, NH_2, and so on. Hence, a very large number of derivatives of ferrocene should be possible. Since the discovery of ferrocene, there has been much activity by organic chemists to develop synthetic methods for preparing such derivatives. As a result of the success of these efforts, many hundreds of such derivatives have now been reported. Workers in this area recognized very early in the game that the cyclopentadienyl rings in ferrocene have "aromatic" character, that is, they behave chemically much like the benzene ring and its derivatives. As a result of this "aromaticity" many of the reactions that have been worked out over the years for introducing substituents into the benzene ring can also be used in ferrocene chemistry. It should be noted in passing that the aromatic character of ferrocene implies that the rings retain a considerable π-electron density. As Wilkinson and Cotton pointed out, this is a strong argument against the donation of all π-electrons to the iron, as in 6.Q.

The organic derivatives of ferrocene are of interest, not only in themselves but also in the light they shed on the structure of ferrocene and the nature of the bonding between the iron and the organic rings in this class of compounds. We cite one example. Richmond and Freiser studied the electric dipole moment (in solution) of the compound 6.R,

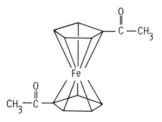

(6. R)

which contains an acetyl grouping in each ring. From a measurement of the dipole moment of 6.S, it is possible to calculate theoretical values

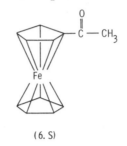

(6. S)

for 6.R, for each of several possible structures, provided the two rings are rigidly fixed with relation to each other. It is also possible to calculate a value, if the rings are free to rotate with respect to each other. This last value is found to be close to the experimentally determined value. Hence, free rotation of the rings in solution must occur.

CYCLOPENTADIENYL COMPOUNDS OF OTHER METALS

The discovery of ferrocene prompted attempts to prepare analogous compounds derived from other metals. The success achieved has been

H																	He
Li	Be											B	C	N	O	F	Ne
Na	Mg											Al	Si	P	S	Cl	Ar
1a	2a	3a	4a	5a	6a	7a		8			1b	2b	3b	4b	5b	6b	7b	0
K	Ca	Sc	Ti	V	Cr	Mn	Fe	Co	Ni	Cu	Zn	Ga	Ge	As	Se	Br	Kr
Rb	Sr	Y	Zr	Nb	Mo	Tc	Ru	Rh	Pd	Ag	Cd	In	Sn	Sb	Te	I	Xe
Cs	Ba	La	Hf	Ta	W	Re	Os	Ir	Pt	Au	Hg	Tl	Pb	Bi	Po	At	Rn
Fr	Ra	Ac															

Lanthanide	La	Ce	Pr	Nd	Pm	Sm	Eu	Gd	Tb	Dy	Ho	Er	Tm	Yb	Lu
Actinide	Ac	Th	Pa	U	Np	Pu	Am	Cm	Bk	Cf	E	Fm	Mv		

Figure 6.8. Metals and metalloids that form cyclopentadienyl compounds are designated by shaded squares.

remarkable, as indicated by the periodic chart of Fig. 6. 8, which shows the elements that have been demonstrated to form derivatives with cyclopentadiene. It is now known that the cyclopentadienyl grouping forms derivatives with more different metals than any other organic group. In addition to those elements commonly considered as metals, Fig. 6.8 indicates that such elements as silicon (Si) and arsenic (As)— both metalloids—also form derivatives. (It is interesting that the potassium derivative was prepared as long ago as 1901, but its unusual structure has only been recognized since the discovery of ferrocene.)

The type of bonding between the metal (or metalloid) and the cyclopentadienyl rings varies widely, depending on the element involved. Cyclopentadienyl derivatives of the alkali and alkaline earth metals have essentially ionic bonds. However, ionic bonding does not prevent the formation of the sandwich structure. Biscyclopentadienyl magnesium, for example, has ionic bonding but a molecular structure similar to that of ferrocene. Cyclopentadienyl sodium, in the solid, has the very interesting structure 6.T; this might be called an "open-faced sandwich."

6. T

The sodium is equidistant from all five carbons. A positive charge is partially localized on the sodium and a corresponding negative charge is delocalized over the ring of five carbon atoms.

The cyclopentadienyl derivatives of the lanthanide elements have three cyclopentadienyl rings per metal atom. All three rings participate in bonding to the metal, with no two rings arranged parallel to each other. Bonding to the metal in these compounds is thought to be ionic.

In addition to the compounds that have only cyclopentadienyl rings bonded to the metal, there are a great many "mixed" compounds that have now been prepared in which other groupings, in addition to the cyclopentadienyl rings, are bonded to the metal. Some of the more exotic of these structures are shown in Fig. 6.9. The numbers on the cyclopentadienyl rings refer to bond distances (in angstrom units) as determined by single crystal x-ray diffraction studies. In the compounds shown, these distances are not equal within the cyclopentadienyl ring. This indicates that some carbons of the ring are more firmly bonded

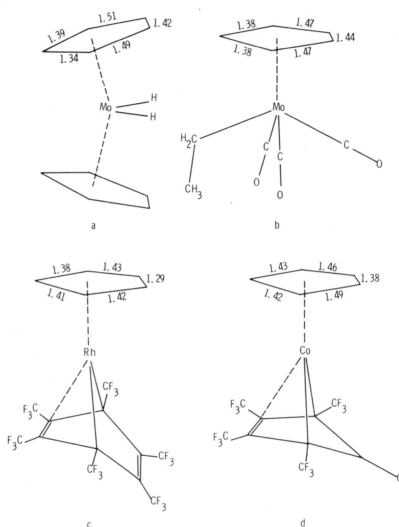

(From *Nature*, *201*, 1318; 1964. Redrawn.)

Figure 6.9. Some cyclopentadienyl compounds.

to the metal atom than are others. This is not the case with the ferrocene molecule. Clearly, much remains to be learned in this fascinating but very complicated area of research.

Finally, we mention that many of the cyclopentadienyl metal derivatives do not share the high degrees of chemical and heat stabilities shown by ferrocene. Some of the compounds react vigorously with water, and must be handled in the absence of air.

BENZENE DERIVATIVES

Prompted by the success achieved in the synthesis of ferrocene, in 1954 E. O. Fischer attempted the preparation of an analogous sandwich compound derived from the six-membered ring substance, benzene. Fischer predicted that the greatest chance of success would be with the metal chromium; he reasoned that the donation of 12 electrons from two benzenes to chromium in the zero oxidation state (6 electrons) would give the stable 18-electron configuration characteristic of the inert gas krypton. By a rather complicated synthetic method, he was able, in fact, to prepare the compound $Cr(C_6H_6)_2$ as a brown-black solid, which is sufficiently volatile and sufficiently heat-stable to be sublimed. Like ferrocene, the compound is soluble in organic solvents but, unlike ferrocene, it oxidizes when exposed to air.

X-ray diffraction studies showed that dibenzene chromium has a sandwich structure analogous to that of ferrocene. A molecular model of this structure is shown in Fig. 6.10.

(Westinghouse Research Laboratories.)

Figure 6.10. Molecular model showing dibenzene chromium structure.

An interesting feature of the dibenzene chromium structure is that, at least formally, the molecule is derived from uncharged benzene and uncharged chromium atoms. This situation is quite different from that of ferrocene, where the compound can be considered to be derived from negatively charged cyclopentadienyl ions and positively charged ferrous ions. In dibenzene chromium, bonding must be entirely due to donation (or sharing) of the electrons of the benzene ring to the chromium atom. Since the initial preparation of dibenzene chromium, similar compounds have been synthesized with molybdenum, vanadium, or tungsten as the central metal atom.

A sidelight to the preparation of dibenzene chromium is that, some twenty-five years earlier, the chemist F. Hein had synthesized a number of chromium-organic compounds. On the basis of elemental analysis, he had assigned the formulas $Cr(C_6H_5)_3$ and $Cr(C_6H_5)_4$ to two of these. The formulas imply that chromium has replaced three or four hydrogens, respectively, in as many benzene molecules. At that time, the structures of these compounds were not understood, and since modern methods of structural investigation were not then available, the question of their structures was allowed to lie dormant for a quarter of a century. Hein's compounds are now known to have sandwich structures very similar to that of dibenzene chromium, with some of the benzene molecules replaced, however, by diphenyl molecules, as indicated by 6.U and 6.V. Thus, Hein's compounds should have been represented by $Cr(C_6H_6)(C_6H_5-C_6H_5)$ and $Cr(C_6H_5-C_6H_5)_2$.

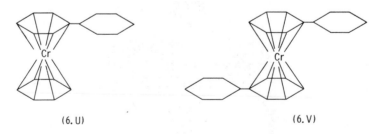

(6.U)   (6.V)

In this connection, it should be noted that in 1954, somewhat before the preparation of dibenzene chromium, H. H. Zeiss and M. Tsutsui of Yale University proposed a sandwich structure for some of Hein's compounds. However, their paper was not accepted for publication at that time, because the journal reviewers did not believe there was

sufficient evidence for the (then) novel sandwich structure. This is another example of how frequently in science discoveries are made nearly
simultaneously, and also how difficult it sometimes is to determine prior-
ity for an idea.

COORDINATION BONDS

A very large group of materials, called *coordination compounds,* or
sometimes "complex compounds," are not only important in the laboratory and in industry, but are also vitally important in the biological
world. (See Chapters Two and Seven.) We can define a coordination
compound as one in which a metal cation (a positively charged ion)
is directly bonded to one or more molecules or negative ions (called
ligands) by means of an electron pair donated by the molecule or the
negative ion.

An example of a coordination entity,° or complex ion, is 6.W, which

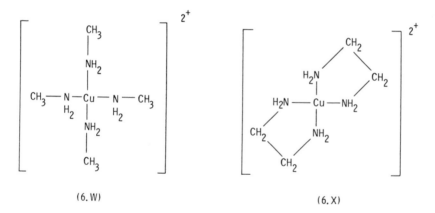

(6. W)   (6. X)

is derived from the cupric ion and methyl amine in water solution. Here
the copper ion is bonded directly to four nitrogen atoms through the
lone pair electrons present on the nitrogens. A very similar complex
ion, 6.X, is formed by ethylenediamine. Since ethylenediamine donates
two nitrogen atoms per molecule, the copper in 6.X forms part of two
five-membered rings of atoms. Such a ring formation makes 6.X more
resistant to dissociation to the amine and free Cu^{2+} than is 6.W, as ex-

° Strictly speaking, the term "compound" should be applied only to solid, electrically
neutral materials, as isolated from solution.

plained in Chapter Seven. Other properties are also affected by ring formation, and for this reason coordination compounds composed of species having metal-containing rings are considered a special subclass, called *chelates* (pronounced "kee-layts").

Both complex ions, 6.W and 6.X, have the same over-all charge of $+2$ as free Cu^{2+} has, since the amines from which they are derived are electrically neutral. Electrically neutral compounds containing these ions, such as $[(CH_3\text{-}NH_2)_4Cu]Cl_2$, however, can be isolated from solution. Here the chloride ions are necessary to balance the positive charge of the complex ion; but they are in no way directly bonded to the copper.

Coordination entities that are negatively charged or electrically neutral are also well known. An example of the latter is the copper chelate 6.Y formed by the amino acid glycine. By the reaction shown, the copper chelate of glycine can be obtained as a blue crystalline non-ionic solid, composed of discrete molecules of 6.Y.

$$H_2N\text{-}CH_2\text{-}COOH \longrightarrow H_2N\text{-}CH_2\text{-}COO^- + H^+$$

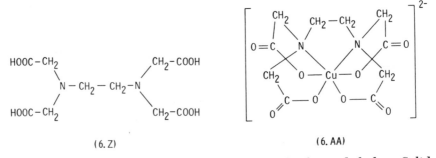

(6.Y)

The water-soluble copper chelate 6.AA, derived from ethylene-diamine-tetraacetic acid 6.Z (usually referred to as EDTA, because of

(6.Z)　　　　　　　　　　(6.AA)

its unwieldy name) is an example of a negatively charged chelate. Solid compounds containing 6.AA, such as $Na_2CuEDTA$, can be isolated from solution. The copper atom in 6.AA is linked to four oxygen atoms and two nitrogen atoms which are part of the same organic chelating agent. (A chelating agent is a chemical compound or ion capable of forming a chelate with an appropriate metal cation.) As a consequence of the linkage to the four oxygen atoms and two nitrogen atoms in the same chelating agent, complexes derived from EDTA are exceptionally stable.

The examples given above involve copper, but most of the metals of the periodic table are capable of forming coordination compounds, although not necessarily with the same complexing agent. The following metals are those most frequently used in coordination chemistry research:

Transition metals: Cu, Ni, Co, Fe, Mn, Cr, Pd, Pt.
Alkaline earth metals: Mg, Ca, Sr, Ba.
Rare earth metals: La, Nd, Eu, Tb.
Metals of group IIB: Zn, Cd.
Metals of group IIIA: Al, Ga, In.
Actinide metals: Th, U.

A wide variety of ligands form complexes with metals, but the atoms actually bonded to the metal are usually oxygen or nitrogen, either alone or in combination, as shown in examples 6.W, 6.X, 6.Y, and 6.AA. Less often, coordination compounds may involve bonding between sulfur, phosphorus, or arsenic, already bonded as part of a molecule, and the metal ion.

There may be 2, 4, 5, 6, 8, or more ligand atoms directly attached to a metal cation, depending principally on the metal and its valence state, but the most common number is 4 or 6. The geometrical arrangement in space, which the attached ligand atoms form with the metal, is a subject studied intensively by coordination chemists, because of its great importance. In the case of four ligand atoms attached to the metal, the atoms may be arranged at the corners of a tetrahedron, as shown diagramatically in 6.BB, or they may be at the corners of a square

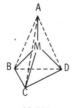

(6.BB)

(6. CC)   (6. DD)

which is coplanar with the metal atom, as in 6.CC. (See Chapter Three.) Six attached ligands are almost always at the corners of an octahedron, as shown in 6.DD. In examples 6.BB, 6.CC, and 6.DD, the letters A through F represent *unidentate* ligands, that is, ligands having only one point of attachment to the metal M. If ligands A through F are identical, only one form of either 6.BB, 6.CC, or 6.DD can exist. If all these ligands are *not* identical, then various arrangements of the ligands about the metal become possible. For example, 6.EE and 6.FF are not identical, although both are planar and each has two bonded A ligands and two bonded B's. The structures 6.EE and 6.FF are referred to as "cis"

(6. EE)   (6. FF)

and "trans" *isomers*. There are many additional possibilities for isomerism, depending on the number of different ligands and their arrangement in space, as well as whether the ligands are unidentate or bidentate (leading to chelate formation). In general, different isomers of the same composition have somewhat different physical properties and therefore can be distinguished from each other in the laboratory. It is possible to predict the number and kind of isomers for a given structure and compare them with what is actually obtained in the laboratory. In this way chemists have been able to show, for example, that complexes having six bonded ligands are octahedral (structure 6.DD) and do not have the alternate possible arrangements 6.GG and 6.HH, since the number of isomers predicted for 6.GG and 6.HH differ from those actually observed.

The spatial distribution of bonded ligand atoms (planar, tetrahedral, or octahedral) is dictated to a large extent by the nature of the metal

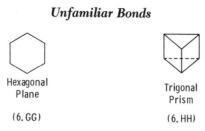

Hexagonal Plane

(6. GG)

Trigonal Prism

(6. HH)

cation; however, it is sometimes determined by the nature of the ligands. An example is the magnesium chelate chlorophyll* (6.II) which

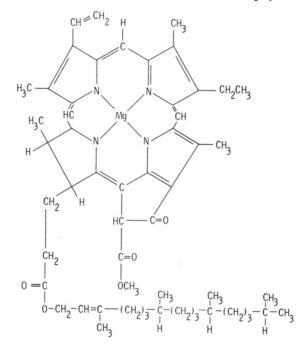

(6. II)

gives plants their green color and is essential to the photosynthesis process, whereby plants convert carbon dioxide and water into carbohydrates. Here the planar arrangement is imposed by the rigid organic portion of the molecule, although normally the configuration about magnesium is not planar. Recently, the American chemist R. B. Woodward and his coworkers have succeeded in the total synthesis of chlorophyll—certainly a major acheivement in chemistry.

* Actually there are two chlorophylls in the higher plants, and these are designated *chlorophyll a* and *chlorophyll b*, respectively.

Since much of our current knowledge of the structure and mode of bonding in coordination compounds has been obtained by physical methods, it is worthwhile to mention a few of these procedures here.

X-RAY DIFFRACTION

X-ray diffraction is one of the most powerful modern methods for studying the structure of solid crystalline materials, either organic or inorganic. (The theory of x-ray diffraction is discussed in detail in Chapter Eight.) While some information can be obtained from polycrystalline powders, complete structural analysis of complicated materials, such as many coordination compounds, requires the use of single crystals. Aside from the difficulties sometimes encountered in preparing suitable crystals, the principal disadvantage of structural studies by x-ray diffraction is the tremendous effort required in the mathematical treatment and interpretation of data. A complete structural determination for a complicated molecular solid, including the atomic spatial arrangement, distances between atoms, and angles between bonds, may take a year or more for a single compound. It should be emphasized, however, that this information can often be obtained in no other way. Modern electronic computers have greatly facilitated the necessary x-ray computations and have made it feasible to study structures of a degree of complexity that would never have been attempted a few years ago.

There are two types of structural information that can be obtained for a solid made up of molecules or polyatomic ions: first, the arrangement of the atoms within the individual molecules or ions: and, second, the arrangement of the molecules or ions within the crystal lattice.

One of the first coordination compounds to be studied by x-ray diffraction techniques was the relatively simple compound K_2PtCl_4. (This work was published in 1922 by R. G. Dickinson of California Institute of Technology.) The structure was shown to be that in Fig. 6.11. Each platinum atom is bonded directly to four chlorine atoms that lie in the same plane as the platinum. The distance from Pt to each Cl is 2.33 Å (or 2.33×10^{-8} cm). The K^+ ions are distributed throughout the crystal lattice as shown and are held by electrostatic attraction.

Later, in the 1930's, much more difficult studies of the organic compound phthalocyanine and its metal chelates were undertaken by J. M.

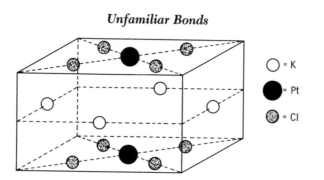

(From *Journal of the American Chemical Society*, 44, 2404; 1922. Redrawn.)

Figure. 6.11. Arrangement of the atoms in K_2PtCl_4.

Robertson. As a result of these studies, the phthalocyanine molecule was shown to have the planar ring structure 6.JJ. In the metal chelates, the metal replaces the two hydrogens in the center of the molecule, as shown in 6.KK. Robertson's investigations are remarkable in that they

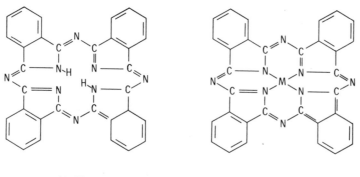

(6. JJ)   (6. KK)

marked the first time that the structure of an organic molecule was determined by a *purely* physical method. (In the treatment used by Robertson it was not even necessary to assume, at the beginning, that the compound was made up of discrete atoms!) However, it should be mentioned, in all fairness, that the phthalocyanines, because of their symmetry and the presence of a heavy metal atom, present a particularly favorable case for treatment by x-ray diffraction. It is often necessary—or at least very helpful—to have information from chemical methods or other physical methods to aid the interpretation of x-ray diffraction patterns.

Since the work of Robertson, increasingly difficult structures have

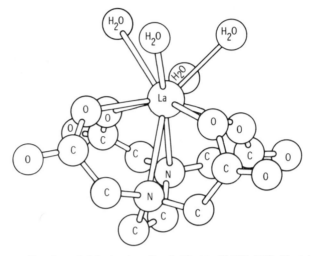

(From *Journal of the American Chemical Society*, 87, 1611; 1965. Adapted and redrawn.)

Figure 6.12. Structure of the lanthanum chelate of EDTA, drawn to scale.

been studied, as experimental and computational techniques have improved. In 1965, the structure of the lanthanum chelate of EDTA, drawn to scale in Fig. 6.12, was published by J. L. Hoard and his coworkers. This is typical of what can now be accomplished.

Surely the most remarkable achievement of x-ray diffraction has been the great strides made in unraveling the complicated structures of the iron-containing proteins, hemoglobin and myoglobin. In both of these materials, iron is bonded as part of a chelate ring system, which in turn is bonded to a complicated protein system, as explained in detail in Chapter Seven. Solving such formidable structures required enormous ingenuity and energy, as well as years of hard work; the results won widespread recognition for the investigators, J. C. Kendrew and M. F. Perutz of Cambridge University, and they were awarded the 1962 Nobel Prize in Chemistry. A drawing of the myoglobin structure as deduced by x-ray studies is shown in Fig. 6.13. The dark object is the heme group, containing the bonded iron, which is surrounded by the protein chain, folded in a complicated manner. Because the resolution of Fig. 6.13 is 6 Å, individual atoms are not resolved. However, continued x-ray study of these vastly complicated molecules is gradually extending the resolution down to atomic dimensions (about 1 Å). There is little doubt that x-ray results, combined with purely chemical studies of structure,

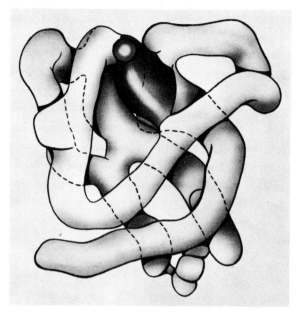

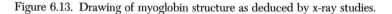

(From *Nature,* *185,* 422; 1960. Redrawn.)

Figure 6.13. Drawing of myoglobin structure as deduced by x-ray studies.

will soon allow atom-by-atom models, much more detailed than Fig. 6.13, to be constructed. (See also Fig. 7.6.)

MAGNETIC SUSCEPTIBILITY

When a substance is placed partially within a magnetic field, it may be strongly attracted, weakly attracted, or weakly repelled from that field. Substances that fall into these three classes are *ferromagnetic,* *paramagnetic,* and *diamagnetic,* respectively. We are concerned here with paramagnetic materials. Paramagnetism is characteristic of compounds having one or more unpaired electrons, that is, electrons whose spins are not balanced by electrons of opposite spin.

In their free, uncomplexed form, a number of metal cations are paramagnetic. Most of those studied have been cations of the first transition period of the periodic table, notably Cu^{2+}, Ni^{2+}, Co^{2+}, Fe^{2+}, Fe^{3+}, and Mn^{2+}. The extent to which the paramagnetism of such ions is altered when incorporated into complexes or chelates provides a valuable tool for determining the extent and type of interaction between ligand and metal. In some instances, the change in paramagnetic character may also give information about the arrangement of the ligands in space.

As a simple example, the Ni^{2+} ion in its ordinary salts, such as $NiCl_2$, has a paramagnetism corresponding to two unpaired electrons. This paramagnetism is essentially unaltered when the nickel forms coordination compounds with many ligands. However, there are some ligands that interact strongly enough with the nickel to force the two free electrons to pair. The resulting compounds are diamagnetic. One such diamagnetic chelate is the interesting compound called nickel dimethyl glyoxime, 6.LL, (used in analytical chemistry for the quanti-

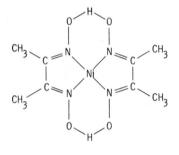

(6. LL)

tative determination of nickel; note hydrogen bonds to the oxygen). (See Chapters Four and Seven.)

At one time it was thought that the formation of diamagnetic nickel was the result of the formation of purely covalent bonds between the nickel and the ligands; nickel complexes were therefore classified "ionic" or "covalent," depending on whether they were paramagnetic or diamagnetic. It is now recognized that this viewpoint is an over-simplification, and much more sophisticated treatments are available, based on ligand field theory. (We mention this only in passing, since a discussion of this theory is not pertinent at this point.)

The experimental determination of magnetic susceptibilities is relatively simple. The sample—usually in the form of a solid, but sometimes in solution—is suspended from one end of an analytical balance so as to be partially within a strong magnetic field. The apparent difference in weight in the presence of the magnetic field, as opposed to the weight obtained in the absence of the field, is directly related to the susceptibility.

SPECTROSCOPY

A good deal of valuable information about coordination compounds has been obtained from their selective absorption of ultraviolet, visible, or infrared portions of the electromagnetic spectrum. (See Chapter Eight for details of absorption experiments.)

If a compound is exposed to infrared irradiation, it will absorb those frequencies corresponding to either the vibrational or the rotational frequencies, or both, within the molecule. Typical infrared spectra for some cyano complexes of cobalt and platinum are shown in Fig. 6.14. In simple cases like this, the relatively sharp absorption peaks obtained can be associated with vibrational modes of diatomic grouping within the complex ions. Thus the spectra of Fig. 6.14 show peaks that result from carbon-nitrogen vibrations, metal-carbon vibrations, and vibrations characteristic of the water of hydration. Spectra from more complicated coordination compounds, especially those derived from organic complexing agents, often contain many more peaks than those of the spectra in Fig. 6.14, and hence are correspondingly more difficult to

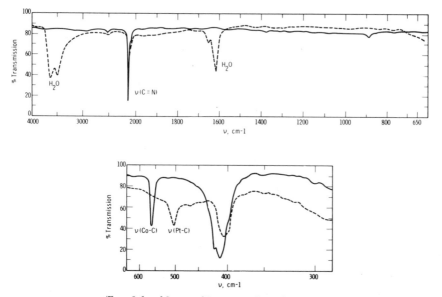

(From *Infrared Spectra of Inorganic and Coordination Compounds*, by K. Nakamoto. New York: John Wiley & Sons, 1963. Redrawn.)

Figure 6.14. Infrared spectra of $K_3[Co(CN)_6]$, denoted by solid line, and $K_2[Pt(CN)_4] \cdot 3H_2O$, indicated by broken line.

interpret. The precise position of absorption peaks along the frequency axis° is often sensitive to the environment in which the grouping finds itself. Thus infrared spectra can give information about whether a particular group is actually bonded to the metal, and may also give information about the relative strength of such bonding.

Selective absorption in the visible portion of the spectrum is due to electronic (rather than vibrational) transitions and is often associated with the bonded metal cation. The visible colors of such ions as Ni^{2+} and Cu^{2+} are the result of electronic transitions of electrons in the $3d$ shell of the ion. When the ion is made part of a coordination compound, the transitions that can occur are affected by the strengths of interaction, as well as the spatial distribution of the bonded ligands; the spectra are correspondingly altered. A study of all of the ramifications of such spectral changes forms a large part of the subject matter of ligand field theory.

Light absorption in the ultraviolet portion of the spectrum is usually the result of electronic transitions within the *ligand,* rather than within the metal ion. Strong absorption usually requires the ligand to be organic. Often the ultraviolet absorption spectrum of an organic complex resembles that of the metal-free organic complexing agent used in its preparation, but the introduction of the metal usually causes changes in the position and intensity of absorption peaks.

Typical absorption spectra for the copper chelate of ethylacetoacetate

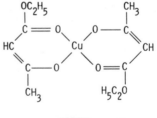

(6. MM)

(6.MM), in both the visible and the ultraviolet, are shown in Fig. 6.15. As a matter of custom, ultraviolet and visible spectra of solutions are often expressed in terms of wavelength and the molar extinction

---

° Infrared spectra are often given in terms of the wavenumber $\bar{\nu}$ which is the number of waves per centimeter. The wavenumber is related to the wavelength (λ) and the frequency (ν) by the equation $\nu = c\bar{\nu} = c/\lambda$, where c is the speed of light.

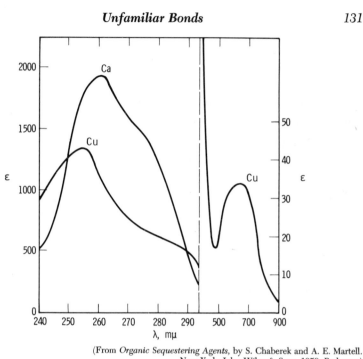

(From *Organic Sequestering Agents*, by S. Chaberek and A. E. Martell. New York: John Wiley & Sons, 1959. Redrawn.)

Figure 6.15. Ultraviolet and visible absorption spectra of 2:1 ethyl-acetoacetates of Cu(II) and Ca(II).

coefficient ϵ, which is defined as $\epsilon = \log (I_0/I)/cl$, where I_0 is the intensity of the light striking the solution, I is the intensity after passing through the solution, c is the concentration, and l is the thickness of the cell containing the solution. While infrared spectra (Fig. 6.14) are often determined for solid materials, ultraviolet and visible spectra are usually carried out with solutions. Note that in Fig. 6.15 the absorption peak at about 252 $m\mu$ (due to electronic transitions within the ligand) is very much more intense than the peak at about 600 $m\mu$ (due to electronic transitions within the Cu^{2+} ion). When calcium is substituted for copper (Fig. 6.15), it causes large changes in the ultraviolet range and there is no absorption in the visible region.

In this chapter, we have discussed only a few of the topics of recent interest to chemists. We have tried to convey some feeling of how research proceeds, and to point out the role that accident and chance sometimes play in scientific work. In this respect, we may contrast the first preparation of ferrocene, which was quite unexpected, with the preparation of the first catenane, which was deliberately sought on the theory that it should exist. The point to be made here is that theory and experiment are inseparable companions. Theory without experiment can lead one far astray and even result in completely wrong conclusions. Experiment without unifying theory can lead only to a chaotic collection of apparently unrelated facts from which little further progress can be expected.

Finally, it is worth emphasizing again the importance of new techniques in studying the structures and the nature of bonding in compounds. Some of the chemist's sharpest tools—infrared and ultraviolet spectroscopy, nuclear magnetic resonance, electron paramagnetic resonance, x-ray diffraction, and electron and neutron diffraction— were either unknown only a few years ago, or relatively undeveloped. Even more sophisticated instrumentation can be expected to find use in the years to come.

In Vivo

EACH LIVING ORGANISM contains a great variety of substances. Yet there is a remarkable unity in biochemistry in the sense that the same, or nearly the same, substances appear in all living forms and perform the same biochemical functions in each. Consequently, we can organize our discussion according to the nature or function of the subject substance, without regard to the form of life—bacterium, plant, or animal —in which it occurs.

We are going to consider some of the chemical bonds in such substances from a qualitative point of view, since a quantitative understanding of these bonds is still lacking in most cases. It would be very useful, of course, to have a really quantitative interpretation so that the effects of small differences in molecular structure could be fully understood. So often it is just some slight difference in structure that leads to a difference in reactivity or function between two biological substances which otherwise look very much alike chemically.

The bonds we will discuss here have all been introduced in preceding chapters; we will simply review them in a new context. Obviously, we will not find exemplified in biology every one of the bond types previously discussed; for example, the metallic state does not occur in living systems (except through surgery and dentistry).

At the outset, it is wise to remember that the bulk of living matter is composed of very large molecules. We can call these *high polymers,* but we should keep in mind that they are very different from synthetic high polymers in which only one or two types of structural unit are joined together in long chain molecules. In biology, the long chain molecule may be composed of as many as twenty or so different structural units, and they are arranged in intricate sequences which help to determine their function. We will not be as much concerned with the main chain bonds of macromolecules as we will with the bonds formed by atoms in the side groups, bonds to other compounds in solutions, bonds to other macromolecules, and even to other side groups of the same macromolecule.

Many of the bonds we are most interested in are very weak; they are readily made and readily broken. They may have only a transitory existence, while one of the reactants is carrying out its function. To appreciate why our greatest interest is in weak bonds, we must remember that all normal life processes occur within a very narrow temperature span of perhaps 40°C, and require no really "strong" reagents. In other words, biochemical processes are rather delicate compared to the methods of synthetic chemistry. But, by the same token, they are very much more specific, the exact direction of a reaction being very sensitive to the bond energies involved and to such subtleties as steric and conformational factors—factors that could well be of minor significance if the same reactants were treated by the more harsh methods of the chemical synthesis laboratory.

The hydrogen bond, one of the most widely encountered and important *weak* bonds, is the first we will discuss.

THE HYDROGEN BOND AND THE PROPERTIES OF WATER

When the organic chemistry student first learns to write formulas, he is given as a firm working rule the fact that carbon forms four bonds, hydrogen one bond, oxygen two bonds, and so on. The rule for hydrogen seems particularly inviolate, because we are all aware that in the hydrogen atom there is only one electron with which it can form a bond to another atom. However, we frequently encounter a situation termed a "hydrogen bond," in which a hydrogen atom, firmly bonded to one atom, forms an additional weak bond to some other atom.

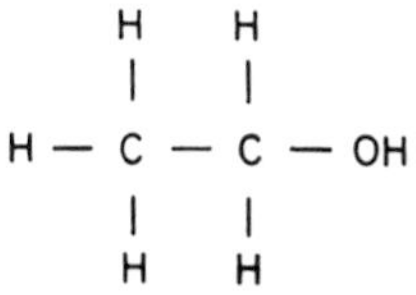

```
        H    H
        |    |
  H  —  C  — C  — OH
        |    |
        H    H
```

Figure 7.1. Structural formula of ethyl alcohol.

Such a concept is generally accepted (even though it seems to violate an old and useful rule) because of the wealth of evidence for such bonds, and because of the striking success of this concept in explaining the anomalous properties of those substances in which these bonds occur. In fact, it was to explain the unusual physical properties of water that the concept was first enunciated over forty years ago.

As an example, let's consider the substance ethyl alcohol, whose structural formula (in accordance with the usual rules) is given in Fig. 7.1. Indeed, if we "look" at the vapor state, we see individual molecules of just that structure. Similarly, these are the molecules we would see in a very dilute solution of ethyl alcohol in hexane. There are Van der Waals forces (see Chapters Three and Five) between the alcohol molecules and the hexane molecules, but they are very weak and also very unspecific; that is, they are not very dependent on the nature of the molecules and are not concentrated between any particular pair of atoms. If, on the other hand, we examine a sample of liquid ethyl alcohol, we find a much stronger force between the molecules. This force specifically ties the hydrogen of the − OH group to the oxygen of a neighboring molecule and is called a "hydrogen bond." Its direction in space is also specific, since it utilizes one of the unshared electron pairs of the oxygen. Hydrogen bonds can form to other negative atoms with unshared electron pairs besides oxygen, notably nitrogen and fluorine. The important examples of hydrogen bonds in biology are those to oxygen or nitrogen.

Since both the oxygen and hydrogen in each OH group can participate in hydrogen bonding, a continuous structure can form, as shown in Fig. 7.2, where the dotted lines depict the hydrogen bonds.

The bonds in the chain are free to rotate so that in reality the chain is not straight, but randomly coiled. Also, since hydrogen bonds are weak, they are constantly breaking and being reformed. Liquid ethyl alcohol, then, is quite different from other liquids containing molecules of the same size which are not hydrogen bonded—propane, for

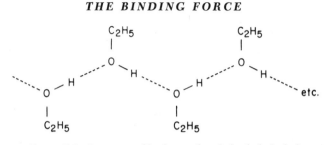

Figure 7.2. Structure of hydrogen-bonded ethyl alcohol.

example. Because the molecules are literally strung together, the vapor pressure is much lower (and the boiling point much higher) than that of propane. (See Chapter Four.) In addition, this "stringiness" leads to a much higher viscosity than that of a nonbonded liquid. Note, however, that the viscosity is not nearly so great as that of a solution of a high polymer (rubber cement, for instance) in which the long molecular chains are formed by bona fide strong bonds, since the hydrogen-bonded links readily snap apart—and join elsewhere—when the shear stress becomes too great. Similar explanations have been successful in clarifying these and other unusual physical properties of the large number of substances that form hydrogen bonds.

If we consider water, rather than ethyl alcohol, a more complicated structure can form, because each molecule has two hydrogen atoms, and in addition to linear structures, we can have branched structures. In fact, there are two unshared electron pairs on the oxygen, and in the small simple water molecule, they both participate in hydrogen bonding. In water, then, the oxygen atom can be bound to its neighbors in four directions, that is, through its own two hydrogen atoms which form hydrogen bonds, and through hydrogen bonds to each of its unshared electron pairs. In the three-dimensional structure thus formed, the oxygen atoms are arranged somewhat like the carbon atoms in diamond (which are bonded to their neighbors in four equivalent directions). When all the water molecules are involved in this three-dimensional structure, we have ice. Since the spacing between oxygen atoms is quite large (one normal bond, plus one hydrogen bond), the density is quite low compared to that of diamond. So much space is wasted in achieving this structure that the density increases considerably when the structure begins to collapse, that is, when the ice melts.

The melting point of ice is much greater than that of substances made up of comparable sized nonbonded molecules, because the structure is held together by relatively energetic hydrogen bonds, rather than just by Van der Waals forces. When ice does melt, only a small fraction—about 10 percent—of the hydrogen bonds are broken, so that liquid water at ordinary temperatures consists of aggregates which, to a large extent, retain the three-dimensional order present in ice.

Usually, as we raise the temperature of a substance, increasing thermal agitation increases the average spacing of the molecules, and the density decreases. In liquid water just above its melting point, however, this effect is more than compensated for by an increase in density caused by the further collapse of the hydrogen-bonded structure. At 4°C, the density reaches a maximum, after which the normal effect of thermal agitation becomes dominant.

The unusual density changes occurring upon the cooling and freezing of water have obvious and profound geological consequences. If ice did not float in water, it would soon fill up natural bodies of water, except for a shallow melted layer on top. The biological consequences are even more profound. Because ice floats and insulates the water below, the predominantly liquid water environment exists on earth, in which life as we know it has evolved.

Since water, the universal biological medium, forms hydrogen bonds so readily, such bonds must play a dominant role in the solubility, suspendibility, and swelling of biological substances in water. Water indeed comes close to being the universal solvent. It has been explained that water dissolves salts and other ionic substances because of its large dielectric constant, which promotes ionization. But we must credit the formation of hydrogen bonds for water's great solvent effect on the many organic substances that it dissolves, including some with very large molecules, such as polysaccharides (starch) and proteins (gelatin). The actual behavior of a biological polymer in a potential solvent depends on a delicate balance of factors, since the formation of hydrogen bonds with the solvent must take place at the expense of the breaking of hydrogen bonds between units of the same molecule. (Hydrogen bonds are also discussed in Chapter Four.)

THE FOUR DEGREES OF STRUCTURE IN PROTEIN

Proteins are very large molecules, formed by the polymerization of some twenty different structural units, the *amino acids*. In addition, we know that they can be isolated in crystalline form, but that both the form and the biological activity are very easily destroyed by heat or chemical reagents, without the molecules themselves being destroyed —a phenomenon known as *denaturation*. When we speak of the *primary* structure, we mean the sequence of amino acids which are joined, by conventional chemical bonds, to form the long-chain polypeptide molecules. This sequence was first worked out by the English biochemist, Frederick Sanger, for insulin, and has now been worked out for several other proteins as well; it remains a continuing task in biochemistry.

All amino acids that form protein have an *amine group* on the carbon adjacent to the *carboxyl group*. The peptide linkage that joins amino acids in a polypeptide chain is made by eliminating water from two molecules, the OH from the carboxyl (COOH) group and the H from the amine $(-NH_2)$ group to form a carbon-nitrogen bond. When writing the above structure on paper, one ordinarily draws a single bond between the carbon and nitrogen, although actually the electron distribution is something in between the two structures shown in Fig. 7.3. As a result, the carbon-nitrogen bond has considerable double-bond character; it is not free to rotate, and the six atoms shown must all lie in the same plane. This geometric restriction was an important clue in deducing the secondary structure.

When we refer to a *secondary* structure, we mean the relative positions in space of neighboring atoms, the same idea to which we unambiguously apply the term "crystal structure" in inorganic chemistry. A polypeptide can crystallize by coiling up to form a helix. The famous α-helix structure was very precisely elucidated by Pauling and Corey, and can best be understood by referring to the structure pictured in Fig. 7.4. The form of the helix is independent of the nature of the side

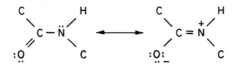

Figure 7.3. Resonance forms of the peptide bond.

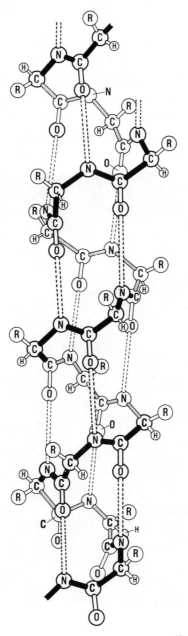

Figure 7.4. Alpha helix structure of polypeptide. The dotted lines represent hydrogen bonds, in which the hydrogen atom is not shown.

chains. (The side chain is all of the amino acid molecule except the carboxyl group, the adjacent carbon, and its amine group.) The tightness of coiling of the chain is such that 18 links are included in 5 turns, each link corresponding to one amino acid residue. The coil is held in place by hydrogen bonds involving an amine hydrogen and a carboxyl oxygen, all the amine and carboxyl groups being utilized for this purpose. The molecule is coiled in such a fashion that each amine group is combined with a carboxyl group four units ahead in the chain. Since there are 3 amino acid *residues*, or links in the chain, between hy-

(From *The World of the Electron Microscope*, by Ralph W. G. Wyckoff. Yale University Press, 1958. By permission.)

A crystal of tobacco necrosis virus. The fact that all of the molecules are identical allows them to line up in an almost perfect array. Magnification 110,000 ×.

drogen bonds and 3.6 amino acid residues per turn, the hydrogen bonds are almost (but not quite) parallel to the axis of the helix.

The way in which the helical segments are folded is called the *tertiary* structure, and the combining of two or more polypeptide molecules (of the same kind or different) into one large particle is called the *quaternary* structure.

If there were no structure beyond that of the helix, all protein molecules would have the same shape—long slender rods. Yet proteins are found in a wide variety of shapes, including the familiar globular class, which includes most enzymes. At first, we might suppose that a spherical shape is the result of the random coiling of the long chain molecules. In the case of a synthetic polymer, such as polystyrene in benzene solution, this is indeed the situation. However, the proteins represent just the opposite situation. Even though it may resemble a ball of string in its complexity, each molecule of a particular enzyme, for example, is just like every other with regard to all details of its conformation. Each twist and turn is duplicated, and is evidently necessary to the complete natural function of the molecule.

Despite the innate stability of the α-helix structure, it can be bent and kinked to conform to the required tertiary structure. One of the weak links in the chain may be *proline*, an amino acid with the structure shown in Fig. 7.5 When it is linked into the protein chain by peptide bonds, it no longer has a hydrogen atom left on the nitrogen, and thus there will be a hydrogen bond missing from the structure.

A crystallized protein is a regular array of molecules which we might aptly describe as "blobs," except that all have exactly the same shape. And since they also have the same internal structure, the positions of each of the atoms can be determined by x-ray diffraction methods. Be-

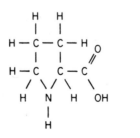

Figure 7.5. Structural formula of proline.

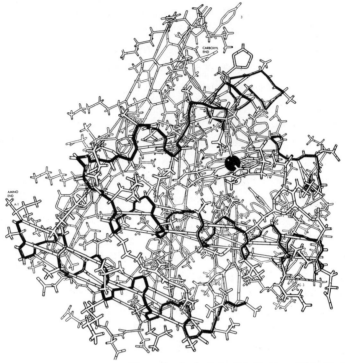

(From a drawing by Irving Geis. Courtesy of *Scientific American*.)

Figure 7.6. Structure of myoglobin molecule determined by x-ray diffraction.

cause of the thousands of atoms in each repeating unit, each determination is a task of heroic proportions, but the result is the most gratifying picture of the tertiary structure possible .Thus, in J. C. Kendrew's picture of myoglobin, shown in Fig. 7.6, we can literally see that the twisting, turning, intricately coiled molecule contains many fairly straight segments with the α-helix configuration.

To build a model of such a molecule, we would use neither straight sticks nor flexible tubing alone, but would assemble instead various lengths of straight sticks joined together by flexible tubing, and then bend this into shape. To hold it in shape would require clamping together various segments of the chain where these touched or came close. Such clamps are required in nature, too, and various bonds between side chains can fill this role, as we will see.

Various bonds, both strong and weak, have been suggested for the purpose of maintaining the tertiary structure. Of these, the only one for which firm evidence exists is the *disulfide* bond, which can be formed from two cysteine side chains. The reaction, which can be considered a mild oxidation, may be depicted as in Fig. 7.7. Such bonds are well known and are very important in the structure of hair and wool. Sanger found three such bonds in the insulin molecule. Two of these link the two otherwise separate polypeptides which comprise insulin. The third links two groups in the same chain. These two groups are only six units apart—and linking them no doubt produces a sharp kink in the chain.

The disulfide bond is strong, and it is comparatively easy to detect because it can survive an analysis of protein composition by chain degradation. Two other types of strong bond could be postulated: (1) amide bonds between residues of basic and acidic amino acids—for example, between lysine and aspartic acid—and (2) ester bonds between residues of hydroxy amino acids and acidic amino acids—for example, between serine and aspartic acid. Such bonds are presumably rare, although one might consider as an example the amide bonds responsible for the highly cross-linked structure found in bacterial cell walls.

In addition to the few strong disulfide linkages, the preciseness of the tertiary structure is undoubtedly maintained by many weak bonds between the side chains. Just because they are weak, their presence cannot be proven directly by any method of analysis that destroys the structure, and the study of their importance is very timely today.

As to the kinds of weak bonds, first of all there are many possibilities for hydrogen bond formation between side chains containing hydroxy, acidic, and basic groups.

Next, there is the possibility that the negatively charged acid groups

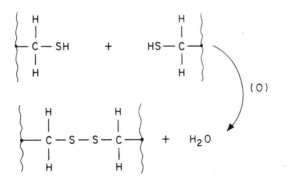

Figure 7.7. Formation of a disulfide bond by oxidation.

of aspartic or glutamic side chains might form saltlike links to the positively charged groups of lysine or arginine. Although we would not expect these groups to interact, particularly in a salt solution, it is not improbable that in the interior of the protein molecule, where the presence of hydrocarbon side chains tends to exclude water and ionic solutes, there may be a potent electrostatic interaction between these ionic side groups.

Finally, a nonspecific bond, called a *hydrophobic* bond, has been postulated. This bond exists for the same reason that molecules of oil, dispersed in water, coalesce into droplets. A large proportion of the side chains are purely hydrocarbon in nature, shown by two examples, leucine and phenylalanine, in Fig. 7.8. Not only are these hydrocarbon portions attracted to each other by Van der Waals forces, but the segregation of these portions from the aqueous phase is energetically favored because it permits the formation of the maximum number of hydrogen bonds between water molecules.

The separated subunits of the *quaternary structure* may be functional proteins, but nature seems to have some subtle reason for assembling them in living organisms. For example, one subunit alone of an enzyme may serve the catalytic function, but only the whole natural enzyme may respond to the cells' control mechanisms. Or perhaps only the complete protein displays the proper antigen-antibody reactions. The bonds between units of the quaternary structure are of the same kind as those supporting the tertiary structure.

Methods of studying these binding forces are necessarily indirect.

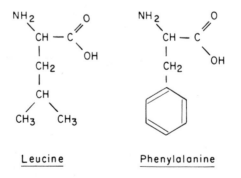

Leucine   Phenylalanine

Figure 7.8. Structural formulas of two amino acids with hydrocarbon tails.

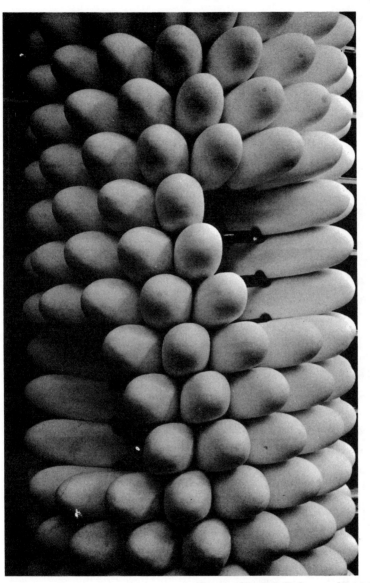

(Courtesy of Dr. D. L. D. Caspar and Dr. A. Klug)

Model of a portion of a single tobacco mosaic virus. The inner black coil, representing the RNA, was exposed by removing several of the protein subunits that make up the coat. Each such subunit is a peptide chain of 158 amino acids folded into an elongated globular shape. The entire virus is 150 angstroms in diameter and 3000 angstroms long.

They are illustrated by the efforts of Dr. Max Lauffer and his colleagues at the University of Pittsburgh to explain the forces that cause the 2200 protein subunits of tobacco mosaic virus to assemble into the tightly coiled string that comprises the outer sheath of the virus molecule. It has been found that this protein sheath can be disassembled and re-assembled even in the absence of the central nucleic acid portion of the virus by mild changes in the pH (i.e., acidity) or the temperature of the solution. A rather striking effect is the clarification of a suspension of virus sheaths upon chilling, and their reappearance when the solution is allowed to warm up again. If we focus attention only on the protein subunits, the results appear anomalous. According to the rules of thermodynamics, all spontaneous processes result in an increase in the entropy, which is the measure of molecular disorder. The virus results are explained by the fact that many molecules of water are released when the protein subunits are joined, so that at room temperatures, the increase in entropy of the water more than compensates for the decrease in entropy of the protein. The extent of assembly of the subunits was followed by observations of optical clarity as well as osmotic pressure. Even the water evolved was measured by an ingenious arrangement in which the difference in weight between assembled and disassembled protein was measured, using a fine quartz spring balance.

The detailed study of the weak bonds that maintain the tertiary and quaternary structures of proteins will require the clever combination of a variety of skills and disciplines. It is one of the most exciting fields of study in biochemistry because of the vital importance of these structures to the correct functioning of such diverse proteins as enzymes, hemoglobin, and antibodies, for example.

NUCLEIC ACIDS AND THE GENETIC CODE

Originally, the study of heredity and genetics meant the gathering of statistics concerning the visually observable characteristics of a controlled population; a "gene" was an abstract concept in the mechanism that explained the results. Later, the physical reality of the genes and chromosomes was observed under the microscope. The next steps were the chemical identification of the genetic material as *deoxyribonucleic acid* (abbreviated *DNA*), and the determination of its physical structure, the double-stranded helix. Finally, much progress has been made in determining just which groupings of monomeric units in DNA correspond to each amino acid in the protein whose synthesis is directed by the DNA. This correspondence is known as the *genetic code.*

The chemical bonds that form the structure of the double helix are well known: phosphate bonds forming the backbone of the DNA polymer, and hydrogen bonds connecting the two strands to each other. This knowledge by no means exhausts the subject, because so much more detail regarding the bonding must be understood before we can appreciate the processes by which the structure forms, reproduces, and carries out its control function, and before we can fully appreciate the specificity and the chances of error in these processes.

The structure of the DNA molecule first depicted by James Watson and Francis Crick in 1953 has since then been supported by many experimental findings. If conceptually we untwist a portion of the helix, we have the ladder structure pictured in Fig. 7.9. The two side rails

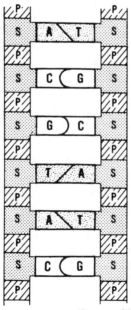

(Courtesy of *International Science and Technology*.)

Figure 7.9. The double-stranded structure of DNA untwisted.

of the ladder are the main chains, consisting of alternating sugar (S) and phosphate (P) groups. Each sugar group bears a side chain base, either adenine (A), cytosine (C), guanine (G), or thymine (T). All of these have the ability to form hydrogen bonds, either as hydrogen donors or receivers. But the shapes of the base molecules are such that adenine fits thymine and guanine fits cytosine particularly well, and also multiple bonds between these pairs are possible. As a result, these matched pairs far dominate all other possible hydrogen bonded pairs. The chemical structures are shown in Fig. 7.10, where the code is the same as in the ladder picture of Fig. 7.9. The particular hydrogen bonds formed are shown, but the molecular fit cannot be fully appreciated except from a three-dimensional model. Note that the hydrogen bonded systems are cooperative in the sense that a planar ring of atoms is set up, in which the hydrogen bonds are nearly linear. Another restriction that prevents mismatching of pairs is the spatial limitation of the helix dimensions. A mismatched pair simply would not fit into the diameter of the spiral formed by the backbone chain.

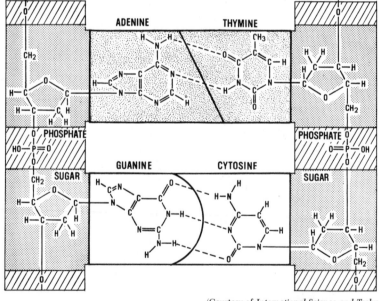

(Courtesy of *International Science and Technology*.)

Figure 7.10. Detailed structural formula of a portion of DNA double strand, showing hydrogen bonds.

The postulate that hydrogen bonds hold the double helix together is strongly supported by the detailed geometry of the molecule as revealed by x-ray diffraction. It is further confirmed by entirely independent evidence, namely, measurements of the energy required to break the bonds. Bond energies fall into three separate regimes. Hydrogen bonds, with an energy of 3 to 4 kcal/mol, are on an order of magnitude or so weaker than most true chemical bonds, and similarly much stronger than Van der Waals bonds. Thus, a classical thermodynamic study of the bond-breaking process will reveal what kinds of bonds are primarily involved. To measure the bond energy requires a measurement of the equilibrium constant over a small range of temperatures for the reaction:

one helix (bonded bases) $\rightleftharpoons$ two single strands (unbonded bases)

Fortunately, it is possible to distinguish between bonded and unbonded forms of the bases in solution, because the unbonded bases absorb ultraviolet light (at about 2600Å) more strongly. This effect is referred to as the *hypochromicity* of the helical form and has become a powerful general tool in studying the degree of interaction of various nucleic acid strands, both natural and synthetic. The structures can be determined and correlated with the hypochromicity by completely independent methods (although with more labor) from the study of the viscosity and light-scattering properties of the solutions. These properties are very sensitive to whether the large molecules are rod-shaped, as in the helix, or randomly coiled, as in the single strands. These methods of measurement, developed in the decades between 1940 and 1960 during the growth of the science of synthetic high polymers, have been rapidly adapted to problems in biophysics in recent years, and have sustained beyond doubt the concept of the helix to random coil transition.

Much of the success of the lines of research mentioned above, and also the successful breaking of the genetic code (discussed below), stemmed from the discovery of enzymes that could catalyze the formation of synthetic nucleic acids. Most of this work has been done with *ribonucleic acid* (abbreviated *RNA*), which differs chemically from DNA because of a slight difference in the structure of the sugar group, and also because instead of the base, thymine, it has a very slightly different base, uracil, which like thymine mates with adenine. RNA does not usually serve as the basic source of genetic information (except in some viruses) but plays a role in the processes by which the DNA directs the synthesis of enzymes in the cell, using the hereditary information in the DNA.

In the following discussion of some of the generally agreed-upon mechanisms involving DNA and RNA, it is not our purpose to try to present a complete physical picture of biosynthesis. Rather, we will point out the many steps at which some subtle change in conditions brings about the assembly or disassembly of the weak bonds of the secondary structure, thus emphasizing how important it is to increase our understanding of these bonds.

To perform its reproductive function, the DNA helix must begin to disassemble in the presence of a solution containing monomeric units. (Each monomeric unit, called a *nucleotide*, contains the sugar and the phosphate, and one of the bases.) Each strand then attracts to itself a set of nucleotides that complement it base for base, and thus duplicates the base sequence of the strand just let go. Simultaneously, the assembled nucleotides polymerize with each other (through sugar to phosphate bonds). The result is a replicate of the original helix, one strand of which has come intact from the original helix, and the other strand of which is new material. At the same time, the other original strand could carry out the same process to reproduce the original. Many elegant experiments have been done using isotopically enriched nutrients to prove that each newly formed DNA helix consists of one old chain and one newly formed one.

For DNA to perform its control function, a portion of a DNA strand (perhaps a partially unwound helix) forms a complementary strand of RNA, called *messenger RNA*. The RNA moves free of the DNA (which remains concentrated in the nucleus of the cell) and into the cytoplasm. There it becomes immobilized on a particle, called a *ribosome*, to perform its synthesis function.

In the cytoplasm there are rather small RNA molecules, called *transfer RNA*. Although these are single strands, they are doubled up like hairpins. At one end of the hairpin is a loop that exposes three free bases. In the middle, the bases mate to form the double helix, thus fixing uniquely for each type of transfer RNA the three bases that are left in the

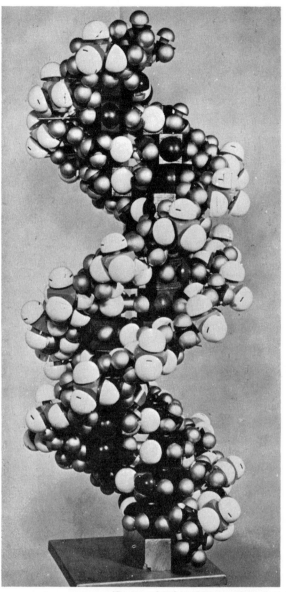

(Courtesy of *Biological Reviews* of the Cambridge Philosphical
Society, and of Prof. M. H. F. Wilkins, King's College, London)

Model of the DNA double helix, showing 16 nucleotide pairs. Carbon, oxygen, and
hydrogen atoms are represented by black, white, and small silver spheres respectively,
and phosphorus atoms are depicted by gray segments. Appropriately shaped blocks
denote the bases that lie between the two parallel spiral chains.

loop. At the other end of the hairpin, the two loose ends of the chain are complexed to a particular amino acid. Each triplet of free bases mates with a triplet of bases on the immobilized messenger RNA, so that corresponding to the sequence of triplets on the RNA there is a sequence of amino acids lying parallel at the ends of a row of hairpins. When this sequence of amino acids polymerizes, we have formed the enzyme that was coded into the messenger RNA and, before that, into the nuclear DNA.

Since 1962, much progress has been made in determining the genetic code, that is, just which triplet of bases and their sequence corresponds to each amino acid. The first break came when it was found that a synthetic messenger RNA containing only the base uracil (U) would select and incorporate into protein only phenylalanine from a mixture of amino acids. Thus, the code word for phenylalanine is UUU. Subsequent work along these lines, using synthetic RNA with other bases, singly and in various proportions, has determined for most amino acids which three bases form the code word.

While we marvel at the perfection of nature in this scheme of things, let's not overlook another, more powerful feature of this scheme—its imperfection. Because the bonds are weak and the differences subtle, mistakes *can be made* and are made in all of these processes, including the replication of DNA. These mistakes give rise to mutations, and by the natural selection of occasional successful mutants, a species evolves. Mistakes can be useful!

POLYPHOSPHATE BONDS AS THE COINAGE OF BIOLOGICAL ENERGY

Energy is required for a number of biological processes, the most obvious being mechanical work such as moving a muscle. It is also required for the transmission of information, such as in nerve action, and for the chemical synthesis of new materials, such as the synthesis of new tissue, or new enzymes, and even of the new DNA for the nucleus of every new cell. In a higher organism, the eventual source of this energy is the chemical energy of the food that is metabolized; in plants it is the energy of the sunlight. Whenever we get down to examining the final steps in any energy-consuming process, however, we find that it

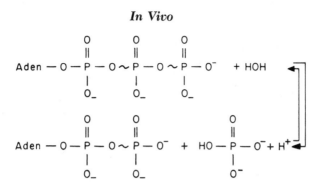

Figure 7.11. Hydrolysis of ATP.

is the very same chemical substance in every case which supplies this energy. This substance, *adenosine triphosphate* (abbreviated *ATP*), performs this function in all living systems, both plants and animals, from one-celled micro-organisms to complex mammals.

To use a broad analogy, suppose we live in an "all-electric home." Regardless of whether the powerhouse operates on coal, gas, sunlight, water, or nuclear fuel, and regardless of whether the energy is used for heat, for work, for chemical change, or for communication, it is the moving electron, in every case, that yields the necessary energy at the point where it is needed. Similarly, it is the ubiquitous ATP that supplies biological energy wherever needed, regardless of the organism's primary source or the nature of the use.

To use another analogy, ATP seems to be the one energy source that is universally negotiable in biological transactions, as acceptable as cash in the market place. But we must be careful not to carry the analogies too far. Complex organisms do not pump ATP through long transmission lines. Rather, ATP performs its energy transport function on the cellular level, the cell receiving its nutrients and oxygen supply, and serving as its own ATP generator. The reason for this is not instability but probably just convenience. ATP is quite stable, can be isolated as a white powder, and can be used to supply energy for biological reaction in a test tube.

The structural formulas shown in Fig. 7.11 illustrate the hydrolysis of ATP to ADP (*adenosine diphosphate*) and P_i (*inorganic phosphate*). The abbreviation *Aden-* is used for the greater part of the molecule, which is not transformed, and is defined in Fig. 7.12.

In Fig. 7.11, "Aden-" means:

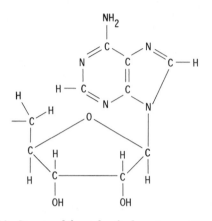

Figure 7.12. Structural formula of adenosine portion of ATP.

Following the custom in biochemistry, certain of the oxygen phos-phorous bonds have been written wiggly ($\sim$) rather than straight ($-$) to indicate that they are sources of energy. The reaction is reversible. After yielding energy, the reaction products can be rejoined to ATP, incorporating energy released in respiration or photosynthesis.

The hydrolysis of ATP, as written above, could result in the release of energy only as heat, unless the reaction were closely coupled to some other reaction that requires ATP energy. The specific enzyme that di-rects the desired reaction also handles the energy transaction by coupling to ATP to become activated. Then, after the desired reaction is com-plete, the ADP is discarded to be regenerated to ATP elsewhere in the cell.

Curiously, ATP is not present in large amounts in the cell. For energy storage, nature prefers *creatine phosphate* or *argenine phosphate*. The balance between these and ATP is so delicate that very little energy is wasted in converting energy in creatine phosphate to ATP. Stated more precisely, the equilibrium constant for the reaction

$$\text{creatine} + \text{ATP} \leftrightarrows \text{ADP} + \text{creatine phosphate}$$

is very close to unity.

A favorite philosophical pastime is to speculate about why certain compounds, or bond types, were chosen by nature exclusively for par-

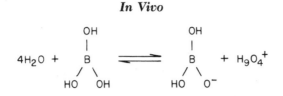

Figure 7.13. Ionization of boric acid in water.

ticular life processes. Let's consider some of the virtues of phosphate bonds, drawing upon some familiarity with inorganic chemistry.

Most anions of a central element surrounded by oxygen are fairly soluble, phosphate being a good example. Certainly a solubilizing group would be required for the universal energy compound, both for the sake of ready availability of inorganic phosphate, as well as for ready transport of ATP and its enzyme complexes.

The choice of phosphate from among other possible ions is determined by the stability of the polyanion, which in turn is determined by the tendency of the corresponding simple acid to ionize. The tendency to ionize can be inferred quite accurately from the number of resonance forms of the anion. (See Chapter Three.) For example, those acids of formula $A(OH)_n$ (usually written H_nAO_n) whose structure consists of a central atom A, surrounded by OH groups, are very weak, with a first ionization constant of about 10^{-7}. Examples are orthosilicic acid, H_4SiO_4, and boric acid, H_3BO_3, for which the ionization reaction (see Chapter Four) can be written as in Fig. 7.13.

On the other hand, if there is one more oxygen than hydrogen, the acid is moderately weak, with a first ionization constant about 10^{-2}. Sulfurous acid, H_2SO_3, and phosphoric acid, H_3PO_4, are examples. Here the possibility of resonance exists in the anion, because of the extra oxygen attached to the central atom, as shown in Fig. 7.14, where the two forms differ by an electron shift.

At the other extreme, if there are two or three extra oxygens (other

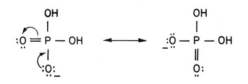

Figure 7.14. Resonance forms of dihydrogen phosphate ion.

than hydroxyl groups) attached to the central atom, as in H_2SO_4 or $HClO_4$, there are, respectively, three or four resonance forms of the anion, and the acid is very strong, that is, the ionization constant is 10^3 or more.

Polymeric forms of these acids are very familiar. These are anhydrides, in which two central atoms share an oxygen between them, as in pyrophosphoric acid, shown in Fig. 7.15. Those acids which have the greatest tendency to ionize also have the least tendency to polymerize, since every sharing of an oxygen atom reduces the possibilities for resonance. (Shared oxygens cannot be double-bonded and so cannot participate in the electron shift exemplified above.) As a result, phosphoric acid which is moderately weak is also moderate with regard to its tendency to polymerize. The dimer of sulfuric acid is very difficult to form and extremely unstable in water solution, hydrolyzing rapidly with much evolution of heat. On the other hand, silicic acid polymerizes spontaneously to a very high polymer and cannot be hydrolyzed except by very strong bases.

Polymeric phosphate salts, such as hexametaphosphate, which form complex ions with the Ca and Mg ions that cause water hardness, are widely used as water softeners and in detergent formulations, because they are both (a) easily enough formed, and (b) sufficiently stable in water. Just as the polyphosphate bond represents the happy medium in formability and stability, the free energy of hydrolysis is also a medium value, about 10,000 calories per mole, very convenient for biochemical processes at body temperature.

We have shown above why nature, once having decided on an acid anhydride bond for her energy coinage, was forced to choose an acid of the strength of phosphoric acid. Indeed, if we consider others in the same class, we find little choice but phosphoric. Acids such as sulfurous and nitrous are powerful reducing agents, unstable to oxidation even by air. The closest analog, arsenic acid, we know precipitates out under biological conditions, and is deadly poison. Carbonic acid is not soluble

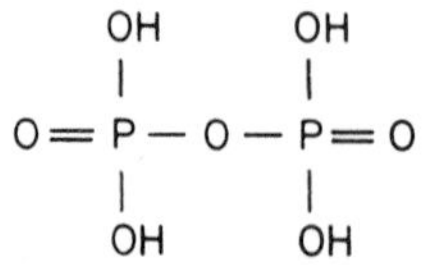

$$\begin{array}{ccc} \text{OH} & & \text{OH} \\ | & & | \\ \text{O} = \text{P} - \text{O} - \text{P} = \text{O} \\ | & & | \\ \text{OH} & & \text{OH} \end{array}$$

Figure 7.15. Structural formula of pyrophosphoric acid.

enough and goes off as CO_2, and the carboxylic organic acids are metabolized. Orthophosphate, however, is widely found in nature, soluble, and very stable to oxidation or reduction.

The choice of ATP must have been made early in the evolution of life, because of its universal presence in all living forms. We understand why the polyphosphate bond was chosen, but what about the rest of the molecule? It must be more than coincidence that adenosine monophosphate (AMP) is one of the nucleotides which are required for the most elementary process of life, reproduction, and must always be present. It is not surprising, therefore, that in recent years the triphosphates of the other essential nucleotides—cytidine, guanosine, and uridine— have been discovered in nature; nor is it surprising that uridine triphosphate plays a role like that of ATP in certain organisms. Why ATP has won out is a very subtle question.

We can next inquire, "Why three phosphate bonds?" The first bond is clearly a low-energy one, similiar in stability to that of most esters of carboxylic acids and alcohols. The second is a high-energy bond that can be readily hydrolyzed, and the third is very similar. For both of these, the free energy of hydrolysis must be in the range of -7000 to $-10,000$ calories per mole, but it has been difficult to measure these precisely and determine the difference. The magnitude of this free energy must be slightly greater for the third bond, and the reason for the third bond must then be that it gives just the right energy for the purpose.

UNUSUAL METAL ORGANIC BONDS

In Chapter Six, we learned that the simple idea of "valence" being the charge on an isolated metal ion was inadequate to explain the wide variety of complexes and complex ions formed by the transition metals. A rather more convenient concept is the *coordination number,* which tells the number of bonds formed by a central metal atom in a complex. This number is more dependent on geometry considerations, that is, size of central ion and coordinating groups, than on the column in the periodic table; the number is most often six for the first transition series. Thus, in a complex ion like ferrocyanide ion, $Fe(CN)_6{}^{4-}$, the central iron atom is bonded to six carbon atoms, which are arranged at the six corners of an octahedron with the iron at the center.

The six iron-carbon bonds are honest-to-goodness strong chemical bonds, although we recognize one important distinction between them and other strong bonds, such as between hydrogen and oxygen in water. In the former case, both of the electrons in the bond come from the carbon atom (or, more generally, from the cyanide ion). It is a coordinate covalent bond. This is the general case for complex ions; we consider them to be formed from simple metal ions, surrounded by groups called *ligands*, each of which has an unshared electron pair with which to form a bond. Other common ligands are ammonia, with an unshared pair on the nitrogen, and water, with two unshared pairs on the oxygen.

Since the coordination number is not dependent on the electrovalence of the ion, it is not surprising to find pairs of complex ions that are identical except for the oxidation state of the central ion, for example, ferrocyanide, $Fe(CN)_6^{4-}$, and ferricyanide, $Fe(CN)_6^{3-}$, or trisphenanthroline ferrous, $Fe(C_{12}H_8N_2)_3^{2+}$, and trisphenanthroline ferric, $Fe(C_{12}H_8N_2)_3^{3+}$, in which the central iron atoms are $2+$ and $3+$, respectively. We notice from these examples that the ligands may be charged or uncharged, and also that the phenanthroline, $C_{12}H_8N_2$, is bidentate, meaning that each molecule forms two bonds (via nitrogen) to the central iron.

The inclusion of a transition metal complex in a biological molecule thereby confers upon it an electronic versatility; nature has taken advantage of this, particularly in enzymes with an oxidation-reduction function, and also in oxygen transport systems.

For any given bond type, the most stable complexes will be those in which the ligands are part of the same molecule. A familiar example is the complex ion formed between Zn^{2+} and $N(C_2H_4NH_2)_3$ (containing four Zn—N bonds), which is much more stable than the complex ion

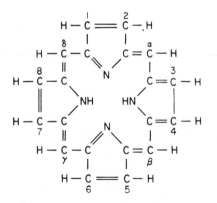

Figure 7.16. Structural formula of porphin.

TABLE 7.A

Biological substance	Metal	Function
hemoglobin	iron	oxygen transport
chlorophyll	magnesium	photosynthesis
cytochrome c	iron	electron-transport chain in mitochondria
vitamin B-12	cobalt	"animal protein factor" "anti-pernicious anemia factor"
peroxidase	iron	reduction of H_2O_2

$Zn(NH_3)_4{}^{2+}$ (also containing four Zn—N bonds). The reason is the very much greater increase in entropy upon dissociation of the latter.

The most common ligand system found in nature for incorporating transition metal ions in functional molecules is that based on the porphin molecule, shown in Fig. 7.16.

In the complex, the metal is bonded to the four central nitrogen atoms (which lie in a plane) and the two hydrogen atoms at the center are removed. The importance of this structure can be appreciated from Table 7.A, an abbreviated list of typical substances in which it is found. In all of these there are various substituents, for example, methyl, vinyl, propionic acid, and so on, in the positions marked 1 to 8 in the formula. In chlorophyll, the basic structure is modified in that positions 6 and γ are part of an additional five-membered ring, and in vitamin B-12 there is no δ carbon, and there are very few double bonds in the rings.

The stability of the metal complexes arises in part from the fact that the four coordinating nitrogens are all from the same molecule. When the two central hydrogens are removed and replaced with a metal ion, it leads to four equivalent bonds to the four nitrogens. This equivalence is indicated by the two resonance forms shown in Fig. 7.17 (in which

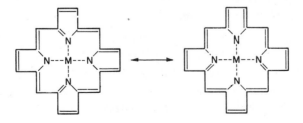

Figure 7.17. Resonance forms of metal-porphin complex.

the carbon atoms are omitted and the symbol M indicates the metal). The argument is completely analogous to that showing equivalence of all the bonds in the benzene molecule, but on a grander scale, since there are four exactly equivalent resonance forms in all, and the metal also participates in the resonance.

The octahedral complexes of iron may be spin-paired or spin-unpaired, depending on whether or not the $3d$ electrons are confined to the minimum number of orbitals or allowed to occupy all five as in the free ion. In the spin-paired condition, the six bonds to the ligands are d^2sp^3 hybrids, utilizing the two available $3d$ orbitals plus the $4s$ and $4p$ orbitals. The tendency is thus very strong for iron, bonded to four aromatic nitrogens (which form spin-paired complexes), to want to make it six ligands. Accordingly, in the natural iron porphyrins (the substituted porphin complexes of iron) there are two reactive positions left on the iron, one above and one below the plane of the nitrogens.

In hemoglobin, the iron porphyrin complex is called the *prosthetic group*, and comprises only a small part of the molecule, the rest of which is a globular protein. Two substituents on the porphyrin ring are chemically bound to the globin, that is, the protein. In addition, it is believed that the iron is coordinated to an imidazole nitrogen in a histidine residue of the protein chain. This leaves the sixth position open for carrying out the function of the molecule. In arterial blood, the iron (which is always in the $2+$ oxidation state) is coordinated to oxygen, but in the veins, it is probably coordinated to water. Carbon monoxide owes its toxicity to the fact that it can also occupy the sixth position, and the binding is so strong that it cannot be displaced by oxygen. Apparently, the entire disposition of the electrons about the iron and the nature of the bonds formed are very sensitive to the nature of the sixth group. It has been found that when this is water, the iron d shell electrons are unpaired, but the more strongly bonded ligands, such as oxygen or carbon monoxide, produce spin pairing.

Much remains to be learned about the subtle influence of the fifth coordinating group (and possibly also the porphyrin side chains) on the properties of the sixth bond. For instance, if the heme prosthetic group is removed from the protein, it can no longer form a stable bond to oxygen, but instead it becomes oxidized very rapidly to the Fe^{3+} state.

Conversely, the formation of the sixth bond has a striking effect on the nitrogen that forms the fifth bond, such that when the sixth bond is to oxygen, the imidazole nitrogen releases a hydrogen ion much more readily. (At physiological pH, this nitrogen is in the form of imidazolium ion, which is analogous to ammonium ion.) We might write the equilibrium reaction as follows, where Hb stands for hemoglobin:

$$Hb + O_2 \rightleftharpoons HbO_2^- + H^+$$

Thus, nature has provided a simple control system. The presence of acid, such as CO_2, will induce the reaction to go to the left, releasing oxygen for use by the cells in respiration. Consumption of oxygen raises the pH and thus solubilizes the CO_2 as bicarbonate for return to the lungs. In the lungs, the high oxygen pressure sends the reaction back to the right, tending to lower the pH and thus releasing the CO_2. The oxygen remains stably attached until the blood reaches a region where oxygen is needed and where the CO_2 concentration is high, which drives the reaction to the left again, starting another cycle.

Despite the apparent similarity between the structures of the hemoglobins and cytochromes, the function of the cytochromes is entirely different, involving alternate oxidation and reduction of the iron during the electron transfer process. It is believed that both positions 5 and 6 are occupied by nitrogen from histidine residues. At any rate, cytochrome *c* does not combine with either oxygen or carbon monoxide. However, there are other cytochromes, differing only slightly in structure, which can react with oxygen and carbon monoxide. Also, each cytochrome has a characteristic redox potential, the values covering a range of about half a volt. Just how this potential is dependent on structure remains to be learned.

Perhaps this chapter has raised more questions than it has answered. If so, it is because biochemistry has just reached that stage where we can ask *why*, in addition to *what* and *how*, regarding molecular structure and chemical changes in living substances. The reason that biochemistry appears to be somewhat behind other branches of chemistry in this respect is simply the immense complexity of living substances. Actually, it is truly remarkable how many structures have been elucidated in detail. Now that we know, for example, that the DNA double helix is held together by hydrogen bonds between bases, it behooves us to learn enough about these bonds so that we can deduce precisely what change in conditions causes them to open up and start the replication process. To a large extent, additional understanding will come from more quantitative measurements of the properties of these bonds. It will no longer be sufficient to know that a hydrogen bond is a weak bond with 3 to 5 kilocalories of energy; we must be able to distinguish quantitatively between dozens of different hydrogen bonds within that span. In many cases, brand new experimental methods will have to be devised to study the bonds of interest. This work is just beginning, and although it may appear an almost endless task, just think of what a task the biochemist faced fifty years ago!

PART
3

Bonds in Sight

Spectral Views

A GREAT DEAL of what we know about the structure of matter in terms of bond strength, shape, and so on, has been learned from the interaction of matter with various types of electromagnetic and particle radiation. The machines designed to measure this interaction have become the basic arsenal of scientists who deal with many aspects of matter. Such devices are used not only to identify the infinite number of materials that exist, but also to make very detailed analyses of them. What are these tools that are now so indispensable to research?

Of the many analytical devices, probably the most commonly used is the *optical spectrograph*. The ultraviolet and visible regions of the electromagnetic spectrum are used extensively in identifying atomic species by their characteristic *emission spectra*. These emission spectra are produced by the excitation of electrons to higher atomic energy levels, and it is interesting that this can be done even when one atomic species is in combination with others. The *absorption spectra* are of still greater interest in the study of gases, liquids, and solids. Typically, these spectra lie within the near infrared region, with wavelengths from about 0.8 micron to 50 microns. Let's see just what an absorption spectrum is and why it tells us something about the bonds between atoms.

A schematic representation of the apparatus used to record the ab-

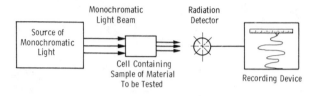

Figure 8.1. Components of an optical spectrograph.

sorption spectrum of a sample of material is shown in Fig. 8.1, and Fig.
8.2 is the actual absorption spectrum of water vapor in the atmosphere.
Each dip in the curve represents a wavelength (photon energy) at which
the water molecule is able to interact in some way with the radiation.
That is, at each of these points the molecule is made to undergo one
of its possible motions by absorbing the energy from the light beam.
A simple example of such a motion is the pulling apart of the centers
of the molecule's polar groups. When this is done, the electrostatic forces
act as a "spring" to restore the molecule to its original shape, as shown
in Fig. 8.3. As a result, the molecule vibrates at the natural frequency

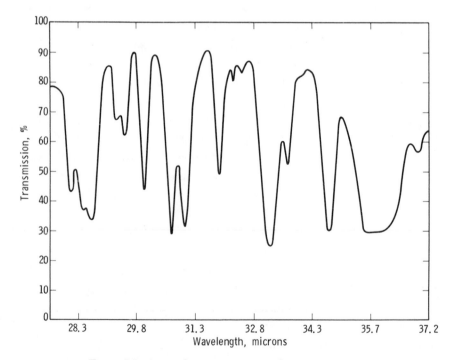

Figure 8.2. Atmospheric water vapor absorption spectra.

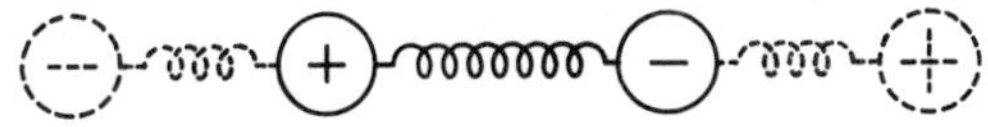

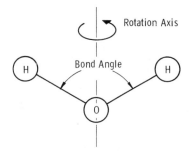

Figure 8.3. Spring model of molecular bond.

of the "spring," or molecular bond. Of course, this frequency corresponds to the frequency of the absorbed incident light, and is measured with the spectrograph. Knowing this frequency and the masses of the constituent atoms of the molecule, we are able to compute the "spring constant" k of the bond from the relation:

$$\text{frequency} = \tfrac{1}{2}\pi\sqrt{k/\overline{M}}, \tag{8.1}$$

where $\overline{M}$ is the effective mass of the atoms. While this is rather a simplification of the actual computation, it is essentially what is done, and it gives some very important information about the molecular bond.

The molecules can also undergo other stretching modes that absorb light at other frequencies, and they can even undergo entirely different types of motion. For instance, they possess the ability to rotate about an axis, as shown in Fig. 8.4, and this is an important degree of freedom. As before, the frequency of rotation corresponds to the frequency of the light at which absorption occurs, so that we can draw still further deductions about the molecular structure, such as the bond angle. By piecing together what can be learned from spectroscopic data with what is known from other sources, it is possible to assemble a remarkably good picture of the molecule. Furthermore, we also have at our disposal the manner in which the spectroscopic absorption bands change with pressure and temperature, which adds a whole new dimension to what can be learned.

Figure 8.4. Rotational motion of water molecule.

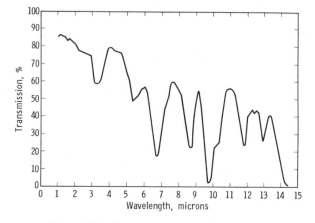

Figure 8.5. Absorption spectrum of benzene.

From the viewpoint of the analytical chemist, an important feature of the spectroscopic absorption bands is that they remain unchanged for most chemical groupings, regardless of combination with other chemical groups. For example, the benzene ring has a characteristic absorption spectrum, as shown in Fig. 8.5, and although the benzene ring is found in a great many compounds, its absorption bands can always be recognized. Such "fingerprints" therefore not only help to identify components of unknown mixtures, but also help in the analysis of unknown compounds by revealing the presence of chemical groups.

Gases and liquids do not differ notably in the ways in which they interact with light, except, of course, that liquids are much denser and therefore absorb much more strongly for a given path length. The feature that distinguishes solids is that their particles are fixed in position and, in crystals, the arrangement is orderly. As we might expect, this order-

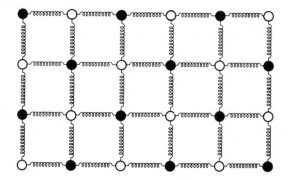

Figure 8.6. Spring model of crystal lattice.

liness influences the ways in which light interacts with solids, and something of the internal order itself can be inferred from this interaction. Take, for example, the sodium chloride crystal, discussed in Chapter Three. We know that bonds between the atoms are not absolutely rigid, so the atoms are able to vibrate back and forth about some equilibrium position. A better dynamic representation of the lattice might be as shown in Fig. 8.6, where all of the springs are identical in length and stiffness. We can see that this lattice can vibrate in an enormous number of different ways. In fact, a detailed mathematical analysis indicates that if there are N particles in the lattice, there are $3N$ different *modes* of vibration possible. The complexity of such a situation is emphasized when we recall that in one cubic centimeter of a solid there are something like 10^{23} atoms, and hence a like number of vibrational modes. Indeed, under thermal agitation, all of these motions are present simultaneously at ordinary temperatures, and the crystal is in a dynamical state that would be simply hopeless to try to describe exactly. Fortunately, for most purposes only broad statistical results are necessary

(Westinghouse Research Laboratories)

An optical spectrograph.

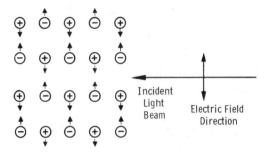

Figure 8.7. NaCl lattice motion caused by light.

to calculate many observable properties, such as the specific heat of a material. As for the optical behavior of the lattice, the situation is even simpler, because theory predicts that of all the 10^{23} or so possible lattice vibrations, there is only one that is capable of interacting with light. In this mode of vibration, all the ions of the sodium sublattice move in unison against the atoms of the chlorine sublattice, which also move in unison. This motion is illustrated in Fig. 8.7 with respect to the incident light beam.

Each of the identical transverse springs is stretched by the same amount at the same time, so the vibrational frequency corresponding to this vibrational mode is given by Eq. 8.1, in which $\overline{M}$ is now the effective mass of one sodium chloride unit cell. Light of this frequency will be very strongly absorbed by the crystal, and measurement then enables us to calculate something about the stiffness of the bonds that hold the lattice together. This type of lattice absorption typically occurs in the infrared from wavelengths between about 10 microns and about 150 microns.

As crystal lattices become more complex in structure than the simple sodium chloride lattice, more complicated optical interactions are possible. For example, a cubic lattice is *isotropic,* which means that it exhibits the same physical properties with respect to the three coordinate directions, so the optical absorption is the same regardless of the direction of the incident light beam. But in crystal lattices that are *anisotropic*—for example, a hexagonal structure, as shown in Fig. 8.8— certain properties of the crystal are direction dependent. In particular, the index of light refraction along the major axis of the crystal is different from that along some transverse direction. In general, bonds parallel to the major axis are not the same as the other bonds, and therefore

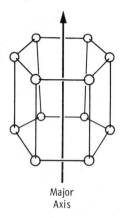

Major
Axis

Figure 8.8. Hexagonal lattice structure.

if the bonding is ionic, the resulting optical absorption for incident light parallel to the principal axis is not at the same frequency as it is for incident light perpendicular to this axis.

In certain ionic crystals, the negative ion may be a chemical radical, such as $(CO_3)^{2-}$, rather than an atom. Calcium carbonate, $CaCO_3$, is an example of such a crystal. Since the bonding is ionic, there is a strong lattice absorption band in the infrared, but it is interesting that there are also absorption bands corresponding to the internal vibrations of the carbonate radical itself, as if it were free of the lattice. Naturally, the rotation bands of the carbonate group are not present, because the group is not free to rotate.

Another interesting phenomenon that may occur when an entire lattice interacts with light is found in crystalline tellurium or selenium. These structures consist of parallel, helical chains of atoms, as shown in Fig. 8.9. When plane polarized light is incident on the crystal par-

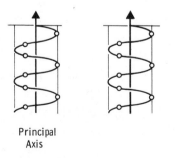

Principal
Axis

Figure 8.9. Tellurium lattice substructure.

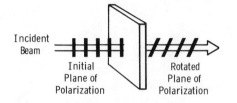

Figure 8.10. Rotation of plane polarized light beam.

allel to the principal axis, the plane of polarization is rotated, and emerges at some angle which depends on the thickness of the crystal. These relationships are shown in Fig. 8.10.

The examples we have described are only a few of the host of possible ways in which light may interact with matter. Properly interpreted, optical data have been among the most useful sources of information about the forces that bind matter together.

X-RAY DIFFRACTION

While spectroscopy has served in the study of chemical bonds in matter, the role of x-ray diffraction has been the determination of the exact location of atoms in relation to one another in matter, particularly in solids. Some of the most strikingly beautiful work in solid state chemistry has been done with this remarkable analytical method, which maps out detailed atomic structure, provided only that the material being studied possesses some regularity in its structure. As we have seen in Chapter Seven, the application of x-ray diffraction to biological problems has been partly responsible for major advances in the life sciences.

Like so many discoveries throughout the history of science, x-ray diffraction was discovered not by any conscious attempt to find it, but rather by accident in the course of another investigation. In 1912, in the course of looking for a means of focusing x rays by passing them through matter, Max von Laue noticed that the x-ray beam produced a pattern of spots on a photographic film. To this day no means of focusing x rays has been found, but the diffraction of x rays by solids, which was evidenced by the spots on the film, has proved of far greater importance. Here was the first concrete proof that a crystal lattice was, in fact, composed of a regular array of atoms. Very shortly thereafter,

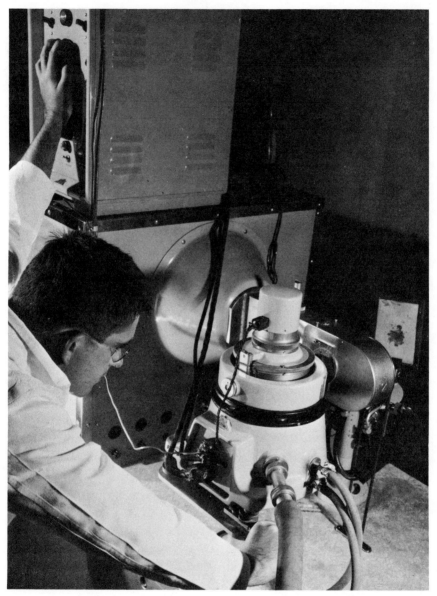

(Westinghouse Research Laboratories)

Crystallographic x-ray machine.

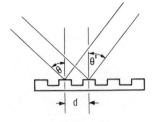

Figure 8.11. Reflection of light by plane grating.

Sir William Henry Bragg made an interpretation by analogy with the diffraction of light by a plane grating.

When a beam of white light is incident on a plane grating, the reflected light is dispersed in a manner indicated in Fig. 8.11. In each order of the dispersion, the light is spread out angularly with wavelength to a degree that depends on the grating spacing. If the incident beam is monochromatic, the reflected beam will appear only at certain angles for which the grating equation is satisfied. Now, a crystal lattice looks very much like a three-dimensional diffraction grating, when we consider that radiation of short enough wavelengths may be reflected off atoms. The spacing of the lattice grating is typically on the order of 5 to 10 angstroms, which lies just within the x-ray region of the electromagnetic spectrum. While the analogy between x-ray diffraction and plane-grating diffraction of light is very strong, there is an important difference in that the x rays are reflected off *planes of atoms*, as shown in the two-dimensional illustration of Fig. 8.12, whereas the light is reflected from grooves in the grating. This figure represents a cubic lattice, and the beam is shown being reflected from planes through the crystal which contain many atoms. Whenever the path difference, 2δ, between the rays reflected from two adjacent planes is an integral

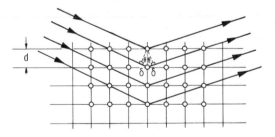

Figure 8.12. Reflection of x rays by lattice.

number of wavelengths of the incident x rays, the reflected rays will be in phase and will interfere constructively. This condition, known as *Bragg's law*, is satisfied when the angle of the incident beam, θ, is given by

$$n\lambda = 2d \sin \theta, \tag{8.2}$$

where λ is the x-ray wavelength, d is the lattice spacing, and n is an integer ($n = 1, 2, 3, \ldots$), called the *interference order*. If a photographic film is placed in the path of the reflected beam, a bright spot will be produced whenever such constructive interference occurs.

The plane shown in Fig. 8.12 is not the only possible one rich in atoms; others are shown in Fig. 8.13 for the same lattice. The distances between the oblique planes relative to the basic distance d are indicated in the diagram, and these would have to be used in the Bragg formula to determine the angles for which constructive interference would occur. When the crystal is rotated in the x-ray beam, the diffracted rays flash out on the film every time the Bragg angle for one of the above crystal planes is reached, *and for each order of interference, n.* In the actual three-dimensional crystal, of course, there are still more atom-rich planes than those indicated in Figs 8.12 and 8.13. Since all of these planes produce a bright spot on the recording film, the resulting spot pattern is a complicated affair, even for the simple cubic lattice. Fortunately, there is more information on the x-ray patterns than simply the placement of the spots; vital data are also contained in the intensity of the spots. Three things primarily determine the intensity of the spot: first, the kind of atom (as determined by its electron structure) located

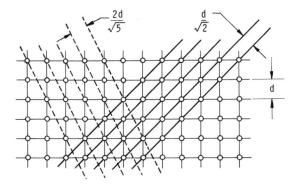

Figure 8.13. Some possible lattice reflection planes.

at the lattice point; second, the density of atoms in the reflection plane, and third, the order, n, of the diffraction. By combining all this information in a rather complicated mathematical analysis, called *Fourier analysis*, the crystallographer is able to determine the type of lattice structure of the particular crystal under study.

Frequently, large single crystals of matter are not available for study, and the scientist has to settle for a powder of the material composed of tiny crystallites. In this case, the widely used method of x-ray *powder diffraction* is very valuable. In this technique, a "pencil" of monochromatic x rays is made incident on the powdered sample, as shown in Fig. 8.14. Since each crystallite is oriented at random, and there are a large number of them in a finely divided powder sample, the reflected beam (when the Bragg condition is satisfied) is not unidirectional but spread out in a cone whose vertex angle is 2θ. The film then records a circle rather than a spot, and the entire pattern consists of a series of concentric circles, each corresponding to a crystal plane and an order of diffraction for which the Bragg condition is satisfied. Obviously, this type of pattern does not contain as much information as the pattern from a single crystal and is not generally useful for crystal structure determination. However, it is very useful for identification purposes, when the powder pattern of an unknown substance is compared with a catalog of the powder patterns of known substances.

As previously mentioned, one of the factors affecting the intensity of the reflected x-ray beam is the type of atom at the lattice points. This is not because of the presence of the nuclei, but rather because of the presence of the electrons surrounding the nuclei. Since x rays are electromagnetic radiation, and the electrons carry electrical charge, they interact very strongly with the electric field of the x-ray beam. The electrons are induced to reradiate x rays because of the periodic motion

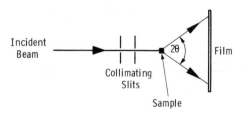

Figure 8.14. X-ray powder diffraction.

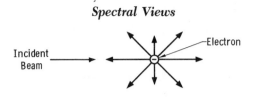

Figure 8.15. Reradiation of an x-ray beam by an electron.

given them by this electric field. The reradiated x rays spread out from the electrons in a pattern similar to that shown for one electron in Fig. 8.15. In this diagram, the length of each line is proportional to the intensity of the radiation in the indicated directions. The curve generated by the ends of the arrows should be rotated about the horizontal axis to create the three-dimensional picture. If we were to record the radiation density distribution on film, it would be possible to locate the electrons' positions at the times they were struck by the x rays.

When an x-ray beam strikes an atom, the situation is considerably more complicated than that pictured, because the atom may have many electrons surrounding it. These electrons may be considered as constituting a smeared-out negative charge distribution, so the electrons surrounding a spherically symmetric atom could be represented schematically by the picture in Fig. 8.16, where the electron density is proportional to the density of the shading. A curve representing the electron density versus the distance from the nucleus is also shown in this figure. Now, when x rays impinge on the atom, every tiny region in the space about the atom reradiates in a pattern like the one shown in Fig. 8.15, where the intensity of the reradiation will depend not only on the direction relative to the incident beam but also on the electron density at the particular point. A film plate will record the integrated x-ray intensity radiated in its direction from all of the regions of space surrounding the atom. If such intensity measurements are

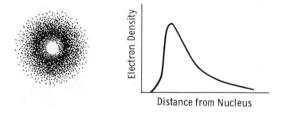

Figure 8.16. Electron density around a nucleus.

made for *all* directions, it is possible to determine the electron density distribution of the atom by using Fourier analysis, the mathematical procedure mentioned previously. This is not difficult for a simple distribution, such as the spherical one illustrated, but it can become quite difficult for more complex distributions, or for those around molecules, which may be very asymmetric.

Let's return now to the question of what happens to the reflected x rays because of the atoms at the lattice points of the crystal. We can see from the preceding discussion that Bragg reflection spots from planes containing heavy atoms will be more intense than those from planes containing light atoms. This is because the heavy atoms are surrounded by many electrons, and hence give rise to a dense electron distribution that reradiates x rays strongly. Therefore, the x-ray pattern provides a means of identifying which atoms are at particular lattice sites, once the structure and chemical composition of a crystal are known. We must understand that determining such details as the electron density distribution around a particular lattice site is a very difficult mathematical task indeed, because the x-ray intensity in any direction is composed of the reradiations of the electron clouds from *all* of the lattice

(Courtesy of K. C. Holmes and D. L. D. Caspar)

X-ray diffraction pattern of tobacco mosaic virus.

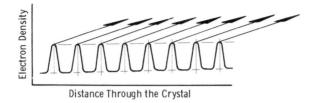

Figure 8.17. Reradiation of x rays by electrons in a crystal.

sites in the crystal, as indicated in one dimension in Fig. 8.17. The only reason the task is possible at all is because the electron clouds are located in a regular periodic array throughout the crystal. Were it not for this regularity, a smeared-out x-ray pattern would result—as is the case for an amorphous solid, or a liquid. It should also be realized that the complete structural determination of a complex material, such as crystallized protein matter, may require thousands of x-ray photographs and years of mathematical analysis involving the use of high-speed computers. We have seen in Chapter Seven what some of the results of this type of laborious but rewarding investigation have been, and shortly we will mention others.

Many of the important properties of solids arise from the vibrational activity of the atoms about their equilibrium positions. Since most features of the x-ray pattern result from the perfect regularity of the crystal lattice, we can see that these vibrations introduce an element of uncertainty about the exact location of the atoms. The effect of this imperfection on the x-ray pattern is a smearing out of the spots (or lines, in the case of a powder pattern). The smearing becomes more pronounced as the temperature is raised, because of the corresponding increase in vibrational activity. In fact, if the temperature is raised so high that the melting point of the crystal is reached, the atoms tear loose completely from their sites, and the x-ray pattern entirely disappears. A certain amount of information about the lattice vibrations— the so-called *phonon spectrum*—can be extracted from the way the intensity distribution of the x-ray pattern changes with temperature.

NEUTRON DIFFRACTION

While it is true that some information about phonons of the crystal lattice can be extracted from x-ray data, the solid state chemist now

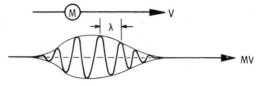

Figure 8.18. Matter wave.

has at his disposal a much more direct method. This very recent development is the diffraction of neutron beams by matter. The underlying
principles of neutron diffraction by crystal lattices are rather similar
to those of optical and x-ray diffraction; the crystal lattice behaves as
a grating from which reflected rays from different lattice planes interfere with one another. The first question that naturally arises, is "How
do neutrons undergo interference effects?" Remembering that interference depends on phase relationships between two beams arriving
at a point, it would seem that we are attributing wavelike behavior
to the neutrons. This is indeed the case, and we can only quote here
the results from quantum mechanics that any moving particle behaves
with certain wave characteristics in which the wavelength is inversely
proportional to the momentum of the particle. To explain this in a more
physical way, we can say that the well-defined particle of classical
physics is described in quantum mechanics as a "wave packet," or
bundle, as illustrated in Fig. 8.18. What this really means is that the
particle location is not precisely known but is statistically distributed
within the wave packet. In most ordinary cases, the extent of the wave
packet is about the same size as the classical dimensions of the particle.
The exact relationship between the particle momentum and the wave
packet wavelength is

$$\text{momentum} = MV = h/\lambda, \tag{8.3}$$

where h is Planck's constant. The wave in question, then, is a matter
wave, which expresses the probability of finding the particle at a particular location at any time. It is not an electromagnetic wave, as the
photon of light is. Still, the matter wave has an important property in
common with the electromagnetic wave, which is that two such wave
packets may interfere constructively or destructively with each other;
in other words, they may undergo diffraction effects.

This is the basis for the phenomenon of neutron scattering by crystals, fundamentally the same as it is for x-ray scattering. The crystal lattice forms a grating for the reflection of the neutron waves. An intense source of neutrons for such measurements is available from a nuclear reactor, which is the reason that this method has been possible only in recent years. In order to achieve a pronounced diffraction effect, it is necessary that the neutron wavelength be about the same size as the crystal lattice spacing. This wavelength is determined by the neutron momentum or, correspondingly, its energy. Since the crystal lattice spacing is on the order of 5 angstroms, a simple calculation tells what neutron energy is of interest. As $\lambda = 5 \times 10^{-8}$ cm,

$$MV = h/\lambda = 6.6 \times 10^{-27}/5 \times 10^{-8} = 1.32 \times 10^{-19} \text{ gm-cm/sec,}$$
$$V = 1.32 \times 10^{-19}/M = 8.25 \times 10^4 \text{ cm/sec,}$$
$$\text{Energy} = \tfrac{1}{2}MV^2 = 5.5 \times 10^{-15} \text{ ergs} = 9 \times 10^{-3} \text{ electron volts.}$$

This is just the range of thermal neutrons, which are plentifully available from the reactor spectrum of neutron energies. The selection of "monochromatic" neutrons is easily accomplished with a mechanical chopper, since their velocity is quite low—on the order of 1000 meters/sec. This chopper scheme is illustrated in Fig. 8.19. A steady beam of neutrons with a wide energy distribution is taken out of the reactor and arrives at chopper *1*, which is a revolving shutter that allows the beam to pass for only a small fraction of each revolution. Chopper *2* is synchronized with chopper *1* so that it is open just when neutrons of the selected velocity have traversed the space between choppers. The beam emerging from the chopper is then composed only of neutrons of that velocity.

The monochromatic neutron beam is made incident on the crystal to be studied, and the beam is reflected from the planes of atoms within the crystal, just as in the case of x-ray diffraction. But there are some important differences between the reflection of x rays and the reflection of neutrons which make these two phenomena complementary ways

Figure 8.19. Neutron spectrometer.

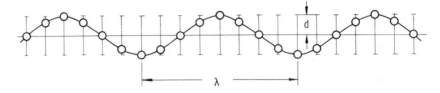

Figure 8.20. Crystal lattice wave.

of looking at matter. First of all, the x rays are scattered primarily by the electron cloud surrounding the nuclei, because the electric field of the x ray interacts strongly with the negative charge. But the neutrons, on the other hand, being electrically neutral, are not affected by the electron clouds and pass right through them. The neutrons interact easily with the nucleus, which is the basis for providing information about the phonon spectrum of the crystal (i.e., the spectrum relating to the motion of the nuclei).

A phonon is one particular mode of vibration of the lattice, characterized by a particular frequency and momentum, and is simply one of an astronomically large number of vibrational modes that a crystal of macroscopic dimensions is capable of supporting. The idea of a mode of vibration can be simply illustrated in one dimension for a single row of atoms, as shown in Fig. 8.20. The displacement d of the atoms from their positions at rest is periodic with the wavelength λ, and in this illustration it is transverse to the line of atoms. The frequency of this vibrational mode will depend on the masses of the atoms and the elastic restoring forces. Energy is carried in this wave, as it is by any vibrating system, and momentum is carried in the direction of propagation of this wave. We can make this plausible by analogy with water waves in the ocean. In a water wave, every particle moves only up and down, perpendicular to the direction of the wave, yet when the wave interacts with something in its path, momentum is transferred in its direction of propagation. This is apparent from the way objects are tossed onto a beach by the action of waves. In the same manner, every lattice wave, or phonon, carries momentum with it.

The behavior of phonons in crystals is complicated by the fact that they undergo *dispersion* in the solid. This idea is not too difficult to understand if we consider a somewhat analogous situation in which light undergoes dispersion in certain media. The velocity of propagation of the light in the medium varies with the wavelength of the light, which gives rise to the dispersing of white light into the spectrum by a prism. We also find in the case of phonons that their velocity of propagation is not a constant, but depends in some fashion on their frequency. Since the phonon momentum is linearly related to its velocity, this results in a nonlinear relationship between frequency and momentum, as illustrated in Fig. 8.21. If there were no dispersion, the curves would be linear everywhere, as indicated by the dotted lines. The analogous situation for light would be that in which the index of refraction of the medium was constant with wavelength.

To understand the dynamic behavior of the crystal, the physicist must know the exact shape of the phonon dispersion curve. This is complicated by the fact that it may be different for different directions in the crystal, that it may change drastically with temperature, and that, even with all of the previously mentioned conditions kept constant, there may be half a dozen or so branches, or separate curves, corresponding to different types of vibrations. The reflection of neutrons by the lattice provides the solid state scientist with the necessary "handle" for this measurement—one that the reflection of x rays is incapable of providing. Because the neutron mass is roughly of the same order of magnitude as the masses of the atoms of which the crystal is composed, a large fractional change of momentum may occur in a collision between the two. Therefore, by measuring the change in momentum of a neutron that is reflected by the crystal, it is possible to infer something about the momentum of the phonon with which it interacted. (Remember, a phonon is really a motion of the crystal atoms.)

Let's consider in a little more detail the quantitative aspects of such

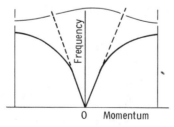

Figure 8.21. Dispersion of lattice waves.

a measurement. First, we must recall that since a phonon is a vibrational motion, quantum mechanics tells us that the energy we associate with it is $h\nu$, where h is Planck's constant, and ν is the frequency of the phonon. By measuring the initial and final energies of the neutron, we can determine the energy of the phonon with which it collided, because conservation of energy allows the relation:

$$E_{\text{neutron, initial}} = E_{\text{neutron, final}} - h\nu.$$

The difference in neutron energies may be measured with good accuracy because, as in the case of momentum, the difference is the same order of magnitude as the initial energy itself. By the principle of conservation of momentum, we can also write the relation:

$$P_{\text{neutron, initial}} = P_{\text{neutron, final}} - P_{\text{phonon}},$$

in which the P's stand for the momenta of the neutron and the phonon with which it collides. Again, the easily measured difference between the initial and the final neutron momentum is a measure of the phonon momentum. So we can see that simply by knowing the velocity of a beam of neutrons before and after it is reflected from a crystal, we are able to determine the energy (or, equivalently, the frequency) and the momentum of a particular phonon. This corresponds to one point on the dispersion curve of Fig. 8.21. By varying the energy of the neutron beam, it is possible to sweep out the entire dispersion curve.

It is now obvious why neutron diffraction complements x-ray diffraction in the study of matter. Because the x-ray photon can exchange practically no momentum with the lattice, it can tell us very little directly about the phonon momenta. An additional important difference between the two is that x-ray diffraction gives little information about the positions of the light atoms, such as hydrogen, because they offer very little electron cloud with which the beam may interact. The neutrons, on the other hand, interact very strongly with the light nuclei, and so give a good indication of their positions in the crystal lattice. The x rays, for their part, offer great versatility in determining atom positions of complex crystal structures. The combination of these two methods allows the research scientist to analyze some of the most complex forms of matter, such as those found in living systems.

NUCLEAR MAGNETIC RESONANCE

Within the past twenty years or so, an entirely new spectroscopy has been developed, based on the magnetic properties of matter. It is called *nuclear magnetic resonance* (NMR), and it enables the scientist to study chemical and physical aspects of bonds that were previously inaccessible to experiment. This new spectroscopy depends on the behavior of nuclear particles in magnetic fields, and its development was actually incidental to the study of these particles. However, the use of magnetic resonance as an analytical tool has far outstripped its use in studying nuclear particles.

To understand this technique, let's focus our attention on the simplest nuclear particle, the proton. For simplicity, we may consider the proton to be a spherically shaped concentration of charge, with a diameter of about 10^{-13} centimeters. This sphere rotates about an axis, much as the earth does, and this rotation gives rise to an angular momentum. The value of this angular momentum is fixed, and is equal to $\frac{1}{2}\hbar$; $\hbar$ is Planck's constant divided by 2π. Since the spinning proton is composed of a charge distribution spinning about an axis, it is equivalent to the circulation of charge in a tiny electric circuit. A current loop gives rise to a magnetic field, and similarly the spinning proton gives rise to a magnetic field. The magnetic field that arises from a charged spinning sphere is illustrated in Fig. 8.22.

The magnetic field of the proton constitutes a *magnetic moment,* and it, too, is fixed in value. This value is given by $(e\hbar)/(2Mc)$, in which e is the charge of the proton, M is its mass, and c is the velocity of light. The neutron also has spin and a magnetic moment, despite the fact that it carries no net charge. We do not know exactly why this is true, but it would appear that the neutron is composed of equal quantities of positive and negative charge, distributed in such a way that

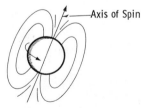

Figure 8.22. Magnetic field of a spinning, charged sphere.

there is a net circulation of charge. In any case, the magnitude of the magnetic moment of the neutron is the same as that of the proton, but opposite in sign. When protons and neutrons are brought together

(Westinghouse Research Laboratories)

Sample container within the poles of an electromagnet used for nuclear magnetic resonance measurements.

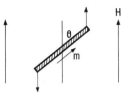

Figure 8.23. Torque on a bar magnet in a magnetic field.

to form atomic nuclei, the angular momentum, or *spin*, as it is called, of the individual particles adds up in a certain way to give the nucleus a resultant angular momentum, therefore a magnetic moment. Generally, the proton spins add up, and the neutron spins add up opposite to the protons, so that the net nuclear spin is the difference between these two. Thus, nuclei that have equal numbers of protons and neutrons have no net nuclear spin, and the magnetic moment of a nucleus will be close to some integral multiple of the basic particle unit, $\mu_0 = (e\hbar)/(2Mc)$, which is called the *Bohr magneton*.

In an external magnetic field, the nuclear magnetic moment behaves, in several respects, like an ordinary tiny bar magnet. A bar magnet of moment m, oriented at some angle θ to an external magnetic field H, as shown in Fig. 8.23, experiences a torque, $mH \sin \theta$, tending to align the magnetic moment with the direction of the field. The lowest potential energy of this system is achieved when the magnetic moment is so aligned. In the presence of an external magnetic field, the nuclear magnetic moment is also in a lower energy condition the more parallel it is to the field. A result of quantum mechanics is that the nuclear magnetic moment cannot be at any arbitrary angle to the external field, but is restricted to certain fixed orientations. If the nuclear magnetic moment is composed of I units, then it can have $2I + 1$ possible orientations with the external field, as shown in Fig. 8.24. In the case

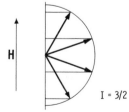

Figure 8.24. Possible orientations of nuclear magnetic moment in an external magnetic field.

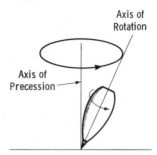

Figure 8.25. Precession of a spinning top.

illustrated in this figure, $I = \frac{3}{2}$. For the hydrogen nucleus, a single proton, $I = \frac{1}{2}$, and there are two possible orientations.

A spinning nuclear particle in a magnetic field behaves very much
like a spinning top or a gyroscope. A spinning top whose axis is tilted
off the vertical undergoes a motion called *precession,* as illustrated in
Fig. 8.25. In this motion, the axis of rotation revolves about the axis
of precession (which is the vertical direction) at some angular velocity
that is related to the rotation velocity, the angle of inclination between
the two axes, and the weight distribution of the top. It is a property
of this type of motion that if we try to tilt the top farther away from
the vertical, it will respond by precessing with a greater angular velocity.
A spinning nuclear particle in a magnetic field bears a similarity, as
shown in Fig. 8.26. The particle precesses about the magnetic field
direction at a velocity ω, determined by the *Larmor angular frequency*
$\omega = \gamma H$, in which γ is a constant called the *gyromagnetic ratio.* The

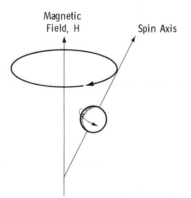

Figure 8.26. Precession of a nuclear particle.

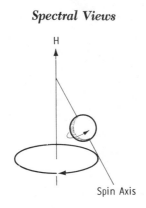

Figure 8.27. Antiparallel spin of proton.

precession frequency, then, depends only on the strength of the magnetic field.

Since the proton has a spin of $\frac{1}{2}$, there are two orientations it may have with respect to the magnetic field: the one shown in Fig. 8.26, and one in which the precession axis is antiparallel to the magnetic field, as in Fig. 8.27. As in the case of the bar magnet, this is a condition of higher potential energy than parallel axes. In order to tip the spinning proton from the parallel axis orientation to the antiparallel one, it would appear that a magnetic force in the direction indicated in Fig. 8.28 would be required (the magnetic field, H_1, producing this force, is in the perpendicular direction). The additional magnetic field will generally not cause the angle of inclination to increase, but rather will cause the rate of precession to increase; this is the same as with the mechanical gyroscope. If, however, the additional magnetic field rotates synchronously with the precession, then it will cause the precession axis to flip to the other orientation. By way of actual numbers, for protons in a static magnetic field of 10,000 gauss, an additional mag-

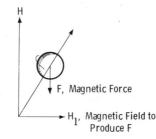

Figure 8.28. Magnetic force on spinning proton.

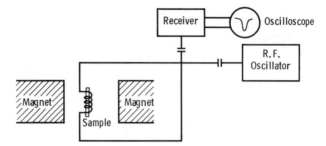

Figure 8.29. NMR spectrometer.

netic field with a rotation frequency of 42.6 megacycles is required to be in resonance with the precessing magnetic moment, and the resonance frequency will be linear with the static magnetic field strength.

These basic ideas of magnetic resonance were known for many years before a simple technique was worked out to actually measure the resonance frequency. This was done in 1946 by Edward Purcell and Felix Bloch, and for their contribution they were awarded the 1952 Nobel Prize in physics. There are several methods of doing the measurement, and the most common one is illustrated schematically in Fig. 8.29. A sample of the material being tested, on the order of a cubic centimeter in size, is placed between the pole pieces of an electromagnet which is capable of reaching magnetic fields of about 10,000 to 15,000 gauss. The sample is surrounded by a coil, one side of which is connected to an oscillator that is capable of generating radio-frequency energy, i.e., about one megacycle to fifty megacycles. The energy that is passed into the coil produces a magnetic field within the coil which rotates about the main magnetic field. If the frequency of this rotating field is just equal to the resonance frequency of the nuclei in the sample material, energy will be extracted by the sample. The signal level is measured by a radio receiver, also connected to the coil, which is tuned to the same frequency as the generator. A more-or-less constant signal level is measured until the resonance condition is met, at which point there will be a sharp reduction, as energy is extracted by the flipping nuclei. The resonance can be displayed dynamically on an oscilloscope by sweeping through the radio-frequency range as the main magnetic field is held constant, or else by slowly sweeping the main magnetic field while holding the radio frequency constant.

This technique of "tuning in" on the proton has allowed scientists to study many things about chemical structure and molecular arrangement in liquids and solids. One of the most important features of magnetic resonance arises from the fact that the magnetic field at which a certain nucleus will be in resonance is determined by not only the field that is applied externally by the electromagnet, but also the contribution by the atoms themselves to the total field. Each nuclear magnetic moment will produce a magnetic field in a neighborhood around itself which will influence other nuclear magnetic moments in that neighborhood. Hence, the total magnetic field felt by any nucleus is the sum of the externally applied field plus the fields due to all the neighboring magnetic moments. In a compound that contains several hydrogen atoms, such as typical organic materials, each hydrogen atom is in a slightly different magnetic environment, so that the resonance will not occur at a sharply defined frequency, but instead will be spread out into a band. An interesting observation, however, is that if the compound is in a liquid form, the resonance will be much sharper than if it is a solid. The reason for this is that in a liquid the molecules are in rapid, random motion, so that the local magnetic field at each of the nuclei averages out to the same value. In a solid, however, the atoms can only move slightly about some fixed position, so in general there is no averaging out of the magnetic fields for different atoms. Thus, if the frequency is held constant while the magnetic field is varied, the resonance region may be as wide as 20 gauss for a solid, and only 10^{-4} gauss for a liquid. This effect is extremely useful for studying the structure of complex crystals. Suppose that a certain crystal contains hydrogen at several different lattice positions. Then if high resolution techniques are used (i.e., very uniform magnetic field and very pure radio frequency), the individual resonances will be seen, each one corresponding to one of the hydrogen lattice positions. By theoretical analysis of the resolved resonance lines, it is possible to identify these positions. This is a useful supplementary tool to x-ray or neutron analysis, both of which are insensitive to light atoms. Here only atoms possessing nuclear moments can be seen by the NMR technique.

One of the important uses of nuclear magnetic resonance to the organic chemist is studying the structure of complex compounds, particularly in liquid form. One of the best examples is the analysis of ethyl

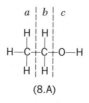

(8.A)

alcohol, $CH_3—CH_2—OH$, whose structural formula is given in 8.A. Since ethyl alcohol is a liquid, its resonance is very sharp, but if it is examined with very high resolution techniques, the spectrum is seen to consist of three distinct proton resonances, as shown in Fig. 8.30.

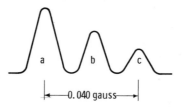

Figure 8.30. NMR spectrum of ethyl alcohol.

Each of the three peaks corresponds to one of the functional groups of the alcohol, whose hydrogen atoms are in slightly different magnetic environments. The ratio of the strengths of the peaks is $3:2:1$, indicating the amounts of hydrogen in each of the groups. The effect in NMR is called the *chemical shift* of the proton resonances, and it is due to the *diamagnetism* of the electrons within each group. An applied magnetic field affects these electrons in such a way that they produce a very slight opposing magnetic field, which tends to shield the protons. This shielding is different for every structural group, hence the amount of shift it produces in the resonance may be used to identify it. Some other simple examples show how this chemical shift is used to identify structure; there are two forms of the compound diketene, $C_4H_4O_2$, whose structural formulas are given in 8.B and 8.C. Each of these has two

$$CH_3—C=CH$$
$$O—CO$$
(8.B)

$$CH_2=C—CH_2$$
$$O—CO$$
(8.C)

lines in its spectra, corresponding to the two groups containing hydrogen, but the ratio of the line strengths in diketene I (8.B) is $3:1$, while in diketene II (8.C) the line strengths are equal, reflecting the hydrogen content in the group of these two forms. Another illustrative example is gallium chloride, $GaCl_2$, in which there exists a chemical shift of the nuclear magnetic resonance of the gallium nucleus. This compound might exist in the two forms given by 8.D and 8.E. In form 8.D, both

$$Ga^+(GaCl_4)^-$$

(8.D)   (8.E)

gallium nuclei are in an identical environment which would lead to only one line in the spectrum, but in form 8.E the magnetic environments are different, so there are two lines in the spectrum. Experiment shows that 8.E is the correct form.

Chemists have found a whole variety of other ways in which nuclear magnetic resonance has assisted in the analysis of chemical systems. Another important use has been in determining the existence of ionic and non-ionic bonds in compounds where both might be present. For example, the hydrated system $BF_3 \cdot 2H_2O$ may ionize according to the formula

$$BF_3 \cdot 2H_2O \rightleftharpoons [BF_3OH]^- + H_3O^+ .$$

In the liquid state, there is about 20 percent ionization. When the material is crystallized, the magnetic resonance spectrum would show two peaks if it were non-ionized, since there are two proton positions in the water. The measured spectrum shows three peaks with an intense central maximum, corresponding to the hydroxyl proton, indicating that the crystallized compound is actually in the ionized state. It is also possible to relate line widths in liquid spectra to bond lengths in their compounds, so certain very detailed structures may be worked out.

So we see that nuclear magnetic resonance is a powerful technique for studying the bond type and arrangement in a wide variety of substances.

ELECTRON PARAMAGNETIC RESONANCE

Spectroscopy involving the magnetic resonance of the nucleus is just one of the two principal types of magnetic resonance which have only recently become available as very useful analytical tools for the physicist and the chemist. Closely related to nuclear magnetic resonance is the phenomenon of *electron paramagnetic resonance* (EPR). In the same way that the proton or neutron generates a magnetic moment because of the fact that it spins, so too does the unpaired electron generate a magnetic moment, because it also has a spin exactly as do the nuclear particles. We have mentioned that the nuclear magnetic moment arises from the fact that a charged, spinning particle is equivalent to a certain electric current, and since the charge of the electron is equal in magnitude to the charge of the proton, we might expect a relation between their respective magnetic moments. The spin, or angular momentum, of the electron is identical with that of the nuclear particles, $\frac{1}{2}\hbar$, but since the mass of the electron is $\frac{1}{1800}$ that of the proton, we might expect that its angular velocity (to the extent that this may be defined for subatomic particles) will also be larger than that of the proton by this same factor. This is indeed the case, and it is expressed by the fact that the Bohr magneton for the electron is

$$\frac{e\hbar}{2mc},$$

in which m is the electron mass. Thus, the ratio of the electron magnetic moment to the nuclear magnetic moment is M/m. In an external magnetic field, the electron magnetic moment behaves the same as the nuclear moment; it is restricted to having the same quantized components along the direction of the magnetic field. The electron magnetic moment of an atom is the sum of the moments of the electrons of which the atom is composed. The electron structure of atoms is generally such that the electrons are paired off in a way that makes their magnetic moments cancel each other. Hence, atoms with completed shells cannot have a net moment; just those atoms that have unpaired electrons have a net magnetic moment.

The rate of precession of the electron magnetic moment in an external magnetic field is faster than that of the nuclear magnetic moment by the factor of $M/m = 1800$, so that whereas the nuclear precession frequency is on the order of several megacycles for an external magnetic field of several kilogauss, the electron precession frequency is on the order of several kilomegacycles. This corresponds to a wavelength of several centimeters for electromagnetic radiation, or the *microwave* region of the spectrum. The techniques used for electron paramagnetic resonance are therefore quite different from the nuclear magnetic resonance techniques. The electromagnetic energy is conducted in rectangular *waveguides*, into which the material is placed. The magnetic field of the electromagnetic wave rotates within the waveguide about the direction of the applied magnetic field, and its energy is absorbed by the precessing electron moment when the resonance condition is fulfilled. A schematic diagram of the apparatus is shown in Fig. 8.31. The resonant cavity is placed between the pole faces of an electromagnet which is capable of field strengths up to 5 or 10 kilogauss. This main magnetic field is modulated at some low frequency by an auxiliary magnet coil powered by an audio frequency sweep generator. The electromagnetic energy is supplied by a microwave oscillator, called a *klystron*, and this energy is conducted by the waveguide to the resonant cavity in which the sample is placed. The electromagnetic energy is reflected from the cavity back into the waveguide and is conducted to a *detector* which measures the amount of energy in the radiation. When the resonance condition is met by the material placed in the cavity, energy is extracted from the microwave radiation, and a lower signal is measured at the detector. As the sweep generator scans through the region of the resonance, a sharp dip is recorded on the strip chart paper at the exact magnetic field value for which resonance occurs.

The high sensitivity of electron paramagnetic resonance is one of the reasons for its great usefulness; as little as 10^{-9} grams of material

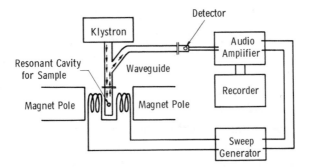

Figure 8.31. EPR spectrometer.

may be detected. Of course, this method is limited to those materials that contain unpaired electrons, and therefore exhibit electron paramagnetism. Most of the materials for which this holds fall into the following groups:

(a) crystals containing bonded atoms of the transition elements,
(b) crystals having broken bonds or defects where free electrons occupy atomic sites,
(c) semiconductors containing electron donor impurities,
(d) metals and semiconductors in which conduction electrons undergo resonance absorption,
(e) free radicals,
(f) ferromagnetic materials.

Electron paramagnetic resonance has been exceedingly useful in the study of crystals, because the electron resonances are determined, as for NMR, not only by the externally applied magnetic field, but also by the local fields within the crystal. A determination of such local fields provides highly useful information for understanding crystal structure. From the point of view of the chemist and the biochemist, perhaps the most exciting use of electron paramagnetic resonance has been the study of *free radicals*. A free radical is formed by a fragment of an otherwise stable molecule; for example, when hydrogen molecules, H_2, are split into their component atoms, the atoms are free radicals. Other free radical-forming molecular fragments are such things as hydroxyl radical, $\cdot OH$, and the methyl radical, $CH_3 \cdot$. Ordinarily, the free radicals are very unstable and live for only a very short time in the free state. The reason for this is associated with their paramagnetism; molecules generally exhibit no paramagnetism because the electrons are magnetically paired in forming the molecular bond, but free radicals contain magnetically unpaired electrons and there are strong forces acting between such electrons to complete a bond. Free radicals play crucial roles in the chemistry of the simplest systems to the most complicated biochemical reactions, but there is no way that their presence may be directly detected, other than through their electron paramagnetic resonance. Thus, the chemist is able to follow the paths of free radicals while they undergo chemical activity, and so it is possible to work out the details of reactions for which only the end products may be experimentally handled.

MÖSSBAUER EFFECT SPECTROSCOPY

The types of spectroscopies we have described so far may be classified in an ascending sequence of characteristic energies, representing a corresponding sequence of tighter and tighter bonds. Thus, neutron spectroscopy utilizes particles of energies up to the order of 0.025 eV, while molecular spectra typically lie in the range up to 0.1 eV; atomic spectra are in the range up to energies of about 20 eV, and the x-ray interactions require energies of thousands of electron volts. The latter involve processes which strip the inner electrons away from the atom, a rather drastic alteration of matter, so it seems that this might perhaps represent the upper limit of energies with which the much lower energies of chemical bonding can be studied. The next higher energy range of radiation takes us into the realm of gamma rays, and these are evolved in processes in which the nucleus of the atom undergoes some change. Just as an atom in an excited state may emit a photon and return to the ground state, so too a nucleus may be in an excited state and return to its ground state by emitting a photon of gamma energy (about 10,000 eV and up). Generally speaking, nuclear events are independent of environmental conditions such as temperature or the chemical state of the atom, so in general we do not expect to derive any chemical information from observing nuclear events. This generality was broken only a few years ago by the discovery of a very special kind of nuclear process.

Let's consider some background in order to understand this new method of looking at chemical bonds. We have already seen that a molecule, for example, can be regarded as a resonating system in which the interatomic bond acts as a spring whose stiffness is determined by coulomb forces. Radiation, whose frequency is the same as that of the molecular resonator, is emitted when de-excitation occurs. Alternatively, if radiation of the resonant frequency is incident on the molecule, it may be raised from the ground state to the excited state. In the same way, the nucleus can be considered a resonant system, in which the forces are much stronger than in the molecule because they are nuclear rather than electrical in nature. Their resonant frequency is correspondingly much higher, giving rise to gamma radiation. One of the important characteristics of this nuclear radiation is that it is of a very sharply defined frequency.

To see what we mean by this, let's go back to the simpler molecular

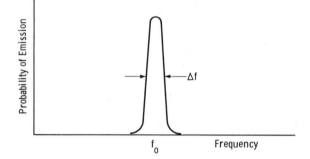

Figure 8.32. Bandwidth of a resonator.

resonator. When we say that its resonant frequency is f_0, this does not mean that it emits radiation of precisely that frequency. Rather, it may emit radiation of frequencies within a certain band about f_0. The probability of emission versus frequency is shown by a typical curve in Fig. 8.32. The width of this curve at the point where the emission probability is down to one-half its maximum is called the half-width, denoted by Δf, and the sharpness of the tuning is given by the ratio $\Delta f / f_0$. For molecules, this quantity may be as low as 10^{-8}; if its resonant wavelength is around 5000 angstroms, then its half-width is about 5×10^{-5} angstroms. It is because f_0 for gamma-ray resonances are so high that their tuning may be so extraordinarily sharp, as small as 10^{-14}. This means that the energy of a gamma ray from such a decaying nucleus will always be the same to within one part in 10^{14}. Now, if gamma radiation emitted by an excited nucleus is fixed to within such a width, it follows that for a nucleus in the ground state to absorb a gamma ray, the gamma ray must also lie within this width; this is the process of *resonance absorption*. When an excited nucleus emits a gamma ray, and if there were no disturbing influences, that gamma ray could be absorbed by a nucleus in the ground state, because it lies within the requisite range. But normally there are disturbing influences. Suppose, for instance, the nuclei are contained within the atoms of a gas. Then the emitted gamma rays will be detuned from their natural sharpness by the random motion of the emitting nuclei in a process known as *Doppler broadening*. This is the same process that increases the frequency of a train whistle when it is approaching a listener and decreases it when the train recedes from the listener. In a similar process, the act of emission itself causes a detuning, because the emitting nucleus must recoil in order to conserve momentum; the gamma photon carries with it a certain momentum, and the nucleus must recoil in the opposite direction with exactly the same momentum. The nuclear mass is many times larger than the mass of a photon, so that the energy the nucleus carries in its recoil is very much smaller than the energy of the photon. This is because the momentum goes as (mass) × (velocity), whereas the energy goes as (mass) × (velocity)^2.

The situation is very similar to the recoil of a gun when a bullet is fired. The gun will recoil in response to the shot, but the more massive the gun the less the recoil will be. In any case, much less energy will be imparted to the gun than to the bullet. Naturally, the energy that goes into the recoil subtracts from the energy that goes into the emitted particle—the bullet or the photon. But because the nuclear resonance is so sharp, this has a very dramatic effect on the resonance absorption of these lower-energy gamma rays by other nuclei. Their energy may be shifted so far that there will be only a very small probability of their being absorbed. This is further aggravated by the recoil that occurs on absorption; when a photon is absorbed by a nucleus, some of the energy of the photon must go into producing a recoil of the nucleus in order to conserve momentum. Hence, the photon must be of energy slightly higher than the resonance energy in order to be absorbed. So gamma rays, emitted by excited nuclei, are doubly shifted in energy relative to their absorption by other nuclei; once by the recoil of the emitting nucleus and once by the recoil of the absorbing nucleus. We may illustrate this shifting with the curves in Fig. 8.33, in which F is recoil shift. The region where two peaks overlap in this figure corresponds to the probability of resonance absorption, so that if the recoil

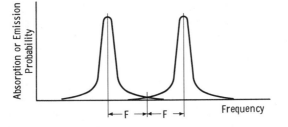

Figure 8.33. Emission and absorption recoil shift.

energy is very large, this overlap region may entirely disappear and there will be no such absorption.

Now, there are some ways we might think of to counteract this effect. For example, suppose that instead of allowing the nuclei to be free, as in a gas, we mix them into a solid material so that their motion is very much hindered. We have already seen that in a solid the nuclei may vibrate about their equilibrium positions, even if they do not migrate away from those positions. This small amount of motion is sufficient to detune the resonance so that very little absorption may occur. When a nucleus bound in a crystal lattice recoils, the energy imparted to the nucleus is dissipated by generating vibrational waves throughout the crystal lattice; these are called *phonons*, in the language we have already used to describe neutron diffraction. We have seen that a given lattice will support only certain phonons, but at ordinary temperatures the density of such phonons is so high that the recoil nucleus has no difficulty dissipating its energy via these phonons.

It was while experimenting with such ideas that the physicist Rudolph Mössbauer made a most astounding discovery in 1957. His experimental apparatus, illustrated schematically in Fig. 8.34, was of the utmost simplicity. The gamma source was a solid material containing the gamma emitter Ir^{191}, the energy of whose quanta is 129 keV. The absorber was of the same material, and behind the absorber was a gamma ray detector which measured the intensity of radiation passing through the absorber, or alternatively, the amount of radiation absorbed. Mössbauer discovered that if the absorber was cooled to the temperature of liquid nitrogen (78°K), the gamma ray detector registered a drop in transmitted radiation intensity. Mössbauer grasped the meaning of this very quickly: when the temperature of the lattice containing the Ir^{191} is sufficiently lowered, it cannot accommodate the phonons necessary for the recoiling nucleus to dissipate its energy. Consequently, the only possible motion available to take up the recoil momentum is for the *entire crystal lattice to recoil as a single massive unit*. Since in a macroscopic piece of matter such as we handle in the

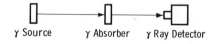

γ Source   γ Absorber   γ Ray Detector

Figure 8.34. Mössbauer experiment.

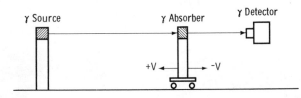

Figure 8.35. Mössbauer effect spectrometer.

laboratory there are something like 10^{22} atoms, we can see that for all practical purposes the process is *recoilless,* and there is virtually no detuning of the resonance, either in emission or in absorption. Thus, in Mössbauer's experiment, the lower intensity measured by the detector indicated that the radiation incident from the source was still in resonance with the absorber nuclei, and so were absorbed by them. This process of *nuclear recoilless resonance absorption* (called the *Mössbauer effect*) has led to the most sensitive measuring device know to man, and it earned the Nobel Prize in physics for its discoverer in 1961.

Let's now see how this effect may be embodied as a spectrometer for measuring very small energy differences. The arrangement is similar to that already shown in Fig. 8.34, with the difference that the absorber is placed in a holder which may be moved relative to the source over a range of velocities. This is shown in Fig. 8.35. If the source and the absorber are identical, then the maximum absorption will occur when the absorber is stationary. If the absorber is moving toward the source, detuning will occur because the incident gamma rays will be of higher-than-resonance energy, and if the absorber is moving away from the source, the gamma rays will be of lower-than-resonance energy. Naturally, the amount of detuning will increase with velocity, and a graph of detector signal versus velocity for Ir^{191}, embedded in metallic iridium, is shown in Fig. 8.36.

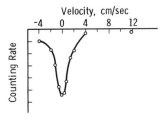

Figure 8.36. Detuning of resonance absorption of Ir^{191} with velocity.

(Westinghouse Research Laboratories)

A Mössbauer spectrometer. The motion is provided by the speaker assembly on the left. The emitter and absorber are located to the right of the larger disk, and the black cylinder on the right is the gamma-ray detector.

We can see that the count-rate of the detector is half its minimum value when the velocity of the absorber is only about one cm/sec. For other kinds of excited nuclei, such changes may occur for absorber velocities of only millimeters/sec or tenths of a millimeter/sec. Of course, the energy differences of the resonances corresponding to these velocities are exceedingly small, and the apparatus shown in Fig. 8.35 allows us to measure these energy differences by measuring the velocity of the absorber.

In the few years since the discovery of the Mössbauer effect, it has been applied to a whole variety of measurements of unprecedented accuracy. For example, in measurements involving time, the preciseness of the gamma frequency provided a clock which, in effect, did not lose more than one second in every 10^{15} seconds. We only mention here that many other applications of this remarkable discovery have been found, without describing them in detail. Let's now focus our attention on some ingenious ways in which the chemical bond has been studied by Mössbauer spectroscopy. We might begin by first pointing out an obvious limitation of the method: we can only study those compounds containing nuclei for which a suitable gamma ray emission exists. Mössbauer effect has been observed in iron, nickel, zinc, tin, tellurium, iodine, rhenium, iridium, gold, the lanthanides, and the transuranium elements. Recoilless resonance radiation is not observed for the light elements, because their gamma energies are too high to be recoilless.

The basis for observing a chemical effect is that the energy of the emitted gamma ray, because it is so sharply defined, is sensitive to changes in the environment of the emitting (or absorbing) nucleus which are too small to be observed by any other means. One such factor is the size and shape of an external electric field at the nucleus. The electrons surrounding the nucleus, including the outer electrons that are responsible for forming chemical bonds, can be regarded as statistically distributed throughout space, with a finite probability of overlapping the region of the nucleus. If the nucleus were merely a geometric point in space, the electron distribution would change the energy of the excited state by exactly the same amount as the ground state. But the nucleus does have a finite size, and furthermore this size is not the same for the excited state as for the ground state. As a result, the electron distribution changes the energy of the excited state and the ground state by different amounts. Since the emitted photon energy is determined by the difference in energy between the two states, a Mössbauer nucleus in two different chemical compounds will emit gamma rays of slightly different energy, because the valence electron structures will not be identical.

A very beautiful example of the application of this is the analysis of the bonding in tin halide compounds containing the active nucleus Sn^{119}. A Mössbauer spectrometer of the type illustrated in Fig. 8.35 was used; the emitter was metallic tin with a small percentage of Sn^{119}. When the absorber was $SnCl_4$, it was found that resonance absorption would occur if the absorber was moving away from the source at a velocity of 2mm/sec. The spectrum shown in Fig. 8.37 was obtained. The energy of the gamma absorbed in $SnCl_4$ is slightly lower than that emitted in metallic tin, which indicates that the electron density at the

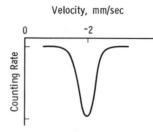

Figure 8.37. Mössbauer spectrum of tin chloride relative to metallic tin.

nucleus is less in $SnCl_4$ than in the metal; this is because a lower electron density gives rise to a smaller electric field, hence to a lower nuclear energy. Thus, the bonding is more ionic in chloride since in an ionic bond the metal atoms tend to give up their outer electrons. Similar studies made on the other tin halides, SnI_4, $SnBr_4$, and SnF_4, yielded different amounts of the Mössbauer velocity (or *chemical shift*, as it is called), indicating different degrees of ionic bonding in these compounds. The Mössbauer velocities are easily converted into energy changes, and from these energy changes it is possible to derive information about the electron distributions for different chemical bonds.

In certain chemical compounds containing Mössbauer nuclei, it is sometimes observed that the velocity spectrum exhibits not one peak but two, and the interpretation of this may lead to important results. For example, in certain oxides of iron, the iron plays more than one chemical role, having valences corresponding to Fe^{2+} or Fe^{3+}. When the active nucleus Fe^{57} is present in such compounds, more than one peak is observed, because a different chemical shift is associated with each valency. Unfortunately (or perhaps it really is fortunate), the presence of a double peak in the spectrum does not necessarily mean that the atom plays a double role. The reason is that there is an effect, in addition to the chemical shift, to which Mössbauer nuclei are subject. This is called *quadrupole splitting*, and we can explain it in the following simplified manner. We have already seen that the chemical shift arises because the nucleus is not confined to a geometrical point in space but has a finite extent. Besides having spatial extent, the electric charge on the nucleus may not necessarily be uniformly distributed in that space. In fact, even if the ground state of the nucleus has a uniform distribution, the excited state may not. A nonuniform charge distribution leads to what is called an *electric quadrupole moment*, which has some important properties on the nuclear scale.

A quadrupole moment is subjected to force in the presence of a non-uniform electric field, which acts to orient the moment in the field. As was the case with nuclear spin, the allowed orientations of the quadrupole moment, with respect to the field, are quantized, only certain directions being allowed. The number of such allowed directions depends on the magnitude of the quadrupole moment, which is also quantized to integral values. Now, a different energy corresponds to each of the allowed orientations of the quadrupole moment in the field, so while in the absence of the field the nucleus was in a unique energy state, that energy state in the presence of a nonuniform field is now split. It is split into as many levels as there are allowed orientations of the moment in the field. Any one nucleus must be in only one of these levels at a particular time, but if there are many nuclei, as in a laboratory sample, then there will be some nuclei in each of the levels. Since the frequency of an emitted (or absorbed) gamma ray depends on the energy difference between an excited and a ground state level, a Mössbauer nucleus will emit (or absorb) as many different frequency gammas as there are energy levels in the quadrupole splitting.

The usefulness of the quadrupole splitting in the Mössbauer spectra of chemical compounds is that it gives an indication of the symmetry of the chemical bonds surrounding the active nuclei, and therefore of the configuration of atoms surrounding them. For example, in a cubic lattice, all of the bonds surrounding any nucleus are symmetrically disposed, so that if they are all of the same type, the electric field at any nucleus will be uniform and there will be no quadrupole splitting. A single peak in the Mössbauer spectrum will result. A most interesting example of a case where splitting does occur is SnF_4. We have seen that a different chemical shift occurs for each of the tin halides because of different degrees of ionic bonding; in all of the tin halides there is a single peak in the spectra, except in SnF_4, which exhibits two peaks. This is because only in the fluoride are the four bonds not all equivalent, leading to an asymmetric electric field at the Sn nucleus, hence to quadrupole splitting. In nuclei in which there are multiple splittings, the spectra are naturally more difficult to interpret, but they are capable of yielding still more valuable information about the nature of the chemical bond.

Our understanding of the chemical bond has evolved largely from studies made with the tools we have discussed in this chapter. These tools have complemented each other so that many different aspects of chemical bonding have been illuminated, all of which will one day lead to a comprehensive theory applicable to even the most complex compounds. It is perhaps worthwhile to note that these sophisticated techniques were discovered and developed in the diverse fields of nuclear physics, atomic physics, solid state physics, and others. They were of primary interest in their own right within these fields, but because they were capable of such powerful analysis in chemistry, they quickly found their way into the hands of the chemist. Thus, in modern science, the growth of one field often provides the stimulus for growth in another area, so that science as a whole benefits.

Taking Stock
of Bonds

ALTHOUGH CHEMISTRY is one of the oldest of the sciences, and the contributions of many workers over the centuries have formed a necessary prelude to our present-day understanding, it is an exciting fact that only in very recent years has an entirely new light been shed on the chemical structure of matter, illuminating in particular the forces that bind matter together. In the preceding pages, we have tacitly assumed that the broad and complex historical foundation, stretching back into antiquity, lends its own validity to more recent developments. We have intentionally concentrated on presenting a modern, integrated view of the chemical bond as an all-pervasive and basic reality of vast importance.

To be sure, we are somewhat in the position of the host who offers his guest *one* peanut—unquestionably nourishing and tasty, though tantalizing. However, we are not assuming that this meager sample will satisfy the craving for more. It is offered with the deliberate intention of stimulating the appetite!

The concept of the chemical bond, as we have described it, permeates all scientific thinking today. But we must bear in mind that we are viewing the picture as it appears at this particular time, although the process of understanding this aspect of nature is in a dynamic state of change, goaded by the development of increasingly refined tools for investigation.

In fact, what has happened—and is now happening—in the study of bonds exemplifies a typical situation in virtually all of the sciences. Ideas developed in physics and quantum mechanics were used to account for the chemical bonds between atoms, and then this brilliant new interpretation was elaborated not only to elucidate much that had been obscure in organic chemistry but also to give deeper insight into observed physical phenomena. In recent years, developments in physics, such as nuclear magnetic resonance and electron paramagnetic resonance, have provided invaluable means for better understanding the nature of bonds, and this increased knowledge has, in turn, stimulated significant advances in other sciences, such as biophysics and biochemistry. Strides in these areas have resulted in new technologies, new techniques, and new materials—and these have found application in physics, thereby raising new questions for physics to answer.

Such feedback and symbiosis are common and very valuable characteristics of science in general. The questioning mind of man has unraveled many of the mysteries that lie at the very basis of life. Although a good start has been made in explaining the complex role of the chemical bond, mysteries still remain. But then, answers in science inevitably raise new questions, and each new discovery stands a chance of touching off a wide-spreading and mutually beneficial chain-reaction in both related and unrelated fields of investigation.

Appendix

Certain Scientists

ARRHENIUS, Svante August (1859–1927) Swedish chemist. Arrhenius, who was a child prodigy, became fascinated by mathematics and physics at a very early age. At the University of Uppsala, he started investigating how electricity passes through solutions, and arrived at the conclusion that compounds (sodium chloride, for instance) in solution break down into charged particles of opposite sign, thus conducting the electricity. He presented his theory of ionic dissociation as part of his doctoral dissertation, but the view was too revolutionary for the time (1884). His professors, aghast at his temerity, gave him the lowest possible passing grade. Not until 1895—after J. J. Thomson's discovery of the electron and Becquerel's discovery of radioactivity—did Arrhenius' theory of dissociation of acids, bases, and salts into parts of opposite electric charge find acceptance. In 1903, he was awarded the Nobel prize in chemistry "for his theory of electrolytic dissociation."

AVOGADRO,Count Amadeo (1776–1856) Italian physicist and chemist, who suggested in 1811 the principle that equal volumes of all gases at the same temperature contain identical numbers of molecules. Avogadro's law was much later elucidated by the Maxwell-Boltzmann law of equipartition of energy, and positively established by the experiments of J. J. Thomson, Millikan, Rutherford, and others. Avogadro's Constant is the number of molecules contained in one mole (grammolecular weight) of a substance.

BERZELIUS, Jöns Jakob (1779–1848) Swedish chemist, whose career proved his amazing versatility. He confirmed by literally hundreds of analyses, and established beyond further doubt, Proust's law of definite proportions. Berzelius compiled the first reasonably accurate list of atomic weights and published it in 1828. He suggested designating the elements by the initial letters of their Latin names (plus one or two other letters, when necessary for clarity). This system is still used today. His views of *radicals* have proved correct in many ways, although his attempt to apply these ideas to organic chemistry was not successful. He discovered the new elements selenium (1818), silicon (1824), and thorium (1829). By 1830, Berzelius had established his reputation as the greatest chemical authority in the world. Many of the chemical terms that he suggested—protein, catalyst, isomer— are commonly used today.

BLOCH, Felix (1905–   ) Swiss-American physicist. Bloch came to the United States in 1934 to become an associate professor of physics at Stanford University. After spending the years of World War II at Los Alamos, he returned to Stanford, and in 1946 published his experimental methods for the very accurate measurement of the magnetic properties of atomic nuclei, not only in gases, but—more importantly—in solids and liquids. This nuclear magnetic resonance method has proved a valuable tool for solving many problems of great technical importance. Bloch shared the 1952 Nobel prize in physics with Edward Mills Purcell (who, working independently at Harvard University, had arrived at a very similar method) "for their development of new methods for nuclear magnetic precision measurements and discoveries in connection therewith."

BOHR, Niels Henrik David (1885–1962) Danish physicist, who applied Max Planck's quantum theory to Rutherford's nuclear concept of the atom, formulating the Bohr theory of atomic structure, and thus laying the groundwork for modern atomic physics. In 1922, Bohr was awarded the Nobel prize in physics "for his studies on the structure of atoms and the radiation emanating from them."

BRAGG, Sir William Henry (1862–1942) English physicist. With his son, William Lawrence, as an associate, Bragg pioneered in the study of crystals by x-ray diffraction. Father and son shared the 1915 Nobel prize in physics "for their contributions to the study of crystal structure by means of x rays."

BROGLIE, Louis-Victor, Prince de (1892–   ) French physicist, especially known for his studies of the wave theory of matter. In 1929, de Broglie received the Nobel prize in physics "for his discovery of the wave nature of the electron," and was also awarded the Henri Poincaré medal. He is the author of more than twenty volumes on physics and the philosophy of science.

BRØNSTED, Johannes Nicolaus (1879–1947) Danish chemist, noted for his significant fundamental contributions to chemical thermodynamics. In 1921, he began studying how acids and bases catalyze reactions. This work eventually led to clarification of the connection between acids and bases, and the recognition that there is only one set of conjugate acid-base systems. Although G. N. Lewis introduced a still broader concept, Brønsted's view is most widely used today.

BUTLEROV, Alexander Mikhailovich (1828–1886) Russian chemist. On a trip through western Europe, Butlerov met Kekulé and became an enthusiastic convert to Kekulé's new theory of structures. Carrying these ideas further, Butlerov applied them to compounds and was the first to refer to the chemical "structure" of a compound.

CAVENDISH, Henry (1731–1810) English chemist and physicist. Cavendish discovered nitric acid, and by inductive experiments combined oxygen and hydrogen into water. He also anticipated a number of later discoveries concerning the nature of electricity.

COREY, Robert Brainard (1897–   ) American chemist, professor of chemistry at California Institute of Technology since 1949. During World War II, Corey worked in a civilian capacity with the Office of Science Research and Development and the U. S. Navy. His major research fields have been the structure of proteins and crystal structure.

COTTON, Frank Albert (1930–   ) American chemist, professor of chemistry at Massachusetts Institute of Technology. Cotton is particularly known for his application of valence theory, and physical and preparative studies to elucidate molecular structures and bonding in inorganic compounds.

COULOMB, Charles Augustin de (1736–1806) French physicist, noted for his experiments on friction and for his researches in electricity and magnetism. He formulated Coulomb's law of the forces existing between charged bodies, and the *coulomb*, a unit of electrical charge, is named for him.

CRAFTS, James Mason (1839–1917) American chemist. While studying in Europe after graduating from Harvard, Crafts met Charles Friedel, who was later to become his partner in research. Returning to the United States, Crafts became a professor at Cornell University and then at Massachusetts Institute of Technology. But in 1874 he joined Friedel in Paris. Their work together on the effect of metallic aluminum on certain compounds containing chlorine resulted in their discovering that aluminum chloride acts as a catalyst for reactions bonding a chain of carbon atoms to a ring of carbon atoms. The *Friedel-Crafts reaction* is of significant importance in the study of chemical synthesis. Crafts later became president of M. I. T., serving in that capacity from 1898 to 1900.

CRICK, Francis Henry Compton (1916–   ) English biochemist. During World War II, Crick worked as a physicist in radar research. Later he joined a group at Cambridge, where revolutionary strides were being made in biochemistry under Perutz, and biology, chemistry and physics were being fused into the new science of molecular biology. In 1953, Crick and his colleague, James Watson, suggested that the DNA molecule is a double helix, each helix consisting of the sugar-phosphate backbone in the nucleic acid molecule. Once it was expained in detail how nitrogenous bases of different sizes are confined to arrangements that result in a double helix of uniform width, the two strands of the double helix unwinding in the process of replication and each single strand serving as a model for its complement, the Watson-Crick model became generally accepted and has led to new and fruitful investigations. For their achievement, Crick, Watson, and Wilkins shared the 1962 Nobel prize in medicine and physiology. Other members of the Cambridge group were awarded the Nobel prize in chemistry the same year.

DALTON, John (1766–1844) English physicist and chemist. In 1793, Dalton published his *Meteorological Observations and Essays*, in which he proposed that the aurora borealis is electrical in origin. His paper on *Absorption of Gases by Water and Other Liquids* set forth the law of partial pressures (Dalton's law). Dalton arranged a table of atomic weights, and was the first to give a clear statement of atomic theory. He discovered the law of multiple proportions and investigated the force of steam and the heat expansion of gases.

DOPPLER, Christian Johann (1803–1853) German physicist and mathematician, professor of experimental physics at the University of Vienna (1851–53). In 1842, Doppler announced his principle that when the source of light or sound waves moves away from an observer, the frequency of the waves appears to become less, and vice versa. This *Doppler effect* is evident for light waves in spectroscopy.

EINSTEIN, Albert (1879–1955) Mathematician and theoretical physicist, born in Germany. Einstein became a Swiss citizen in his youth, and in 1940 he was naturalized as a citizen of the United States. Each of three papers, published when he was twenty-six, became the source of a new branch of physics. Although Einstein is probably most famous for his theory of relativity, he also made significant contributions in other areas, such as the theory of Brownian movement, emission and absorption of radiation, and particle statistics. Einstein was awarded the 1921 Nobel prize in physics "for his contributions to mathematical physics, and especially for his discovery of the law of the photoelectric effect."

EYRING, Henry (1901–   ) American physical chemist, Dean of the Graduate School, University of Utah, since 1946. Eyring has received widespread recognition for his work in the application of quantum mechanics to chemistry, as well as the theory of reaction rates and the theory of liquids.

FEYNMAN, Richard Phillips (1918–   ) American theoretical physicist, Tolman Professor at California Institute of Technology since 1951. Feynman was a physicist on the atomic energy project at Princeton, and then joined the Los Alamos project, where he worked from 1942 to 1945. From then until 1951, he was associate professor of physics

at Cornell University. Feynman is known for his work in quantum elec-
trodynamics, and his studies have included the principle of least action
in quantum mechanics; liquid helium; beta-decay and weak interactions.
In 1965, Feynman shared the Nobel prize in physics with Julian S.
Schwinger and Shinichiro Tomonoga.

FISCHER, Ernst Otto (1918–   ) German chemist. Since 1957, Fischer
has been professor of inorganic chemistry at the University of Munich.

FOURIER, Jean Baptiste Joseph, Baron de (1768–1830) French mathematician, noted for having devised the Fourier theorem, which states
that any periodic oscillation, regardless of its complexity, can be broken
down into a series of regular wave motions whose sum is the original
periodic variation. When this theorem was announced in 1807,
Napoleon—with whom Fourier was closely associated—honored him
with the title of baron in recognition of his achievements and attendant
scientific fame. Fourier's theorem has broad application, in studying
not only light and sound waves but any wave phenomena.

FRANKLAND, Sir Edward (1825–1899) English chemist, noted for being
the first to prepare and study organometallic compounds. This work
led to his valence theory in 1852, which inspired Kekulé structures and
Mendeleev's periodic table. Frankland later turned his attention to
river pollution and did significant work in this area. In 1894, he was
awarded the Copley medal of the Royal Society and was knighted three
years later.

FREISER, Henry (1920–   ) American analytical chemist. Since 1958,
Freiser has been professor of chemistry and head of the department
at the University of Arizona. His research work has included dipole
moments, organic reagents in inorganic analysis, chelate chemistry,
solvent extractions, ion exchange, and chromatography.

FRIEDEL, Charles (1832–1899) French chemist, who was appointed
professor of mineralogy at the Sorbonne in 1876. He is especially known
for his work with James Crafts, which resulted in their discovery of
the Friedel-Crafts reaction. Friedel was one of a number of mineralog-

ical chemists who attempted unsuccessfully to produce synthetic diamonds. His observations on organic compounds containing silicon (which he abandoned) were later developed with notable success by the English chemist Frederick Kipping. (*See also* Crafts.)

FRISCH, Harry Lloyd (1928–   ) Austrian-American physical chemist. Frisch has been a member of the technical staff at Bell Telephone Laboratories since 1956. His work is in the areas of statistical mechanics and kinetic theory, colloid and high polymer chemistry, and solid state chemistry and physics.

GAY-LUSSAC, Joseph Louis (1778–1850) French chemist and physicist, noted for his researches on chemical combinations, iodine, and cyanogen. He enunciated the law that bears his name, stating that gases combine with each other in simple definite proportions.

GULDBERG, Cato Maximillian (1836–1902) Norwegian chemist, professor of applied mathematics at the University of Christiania. Guldberg is especially known for his *law of mass action*, which he and his brother-in-law, Peter Waage, first published in Norwegian in 1863. It made no impression whatever on the chemists of the day, even when they brought out a French translation four years later. Finally, Guldberg and Waage published a full German translation in 1879. Although they were given credit for their work, an understanding of this law had to await the time when the work of J. Willard Gibbs became known.

HEISENBERG, Werner Karl (1901–   ) German theoretical physicist. Heisenberg had an impressive background in quantum theory and its applications to atomic physics. He studied with both Arnold Sommerfeld and Max Born, and later spent a year with Niels Bohr in Copenhagen. Heisenberg's work has had profound influence on the development of atomic and nuclear physics. He received the 1932 Nobel prize "for the creation of quantum mechanics, the application of which has led, among other things, to the discovery of the allotropic form of hydrogen." According to Heisenberg's *uncertainty principle* there are limits to the accuracy with which certain atomic occurrences can be known.

HENRY, Joseph (1797–1878) American physicist, whose poverty and early apprenticeship to a watchmaker was an unlikely beginning for a scientific career. He eventually graduated from Albany Academy, and in 1826 started teaching mathematics and science there. The demands of teaching left him little time for research or invention, but he finally managed to construct an electromagnet, using insulated wire for the first time, which he had laboriously hand-wrapped. Eventually, he succeeded in constructing one that would lift a ton of iron. He then experimented with longer and longer wires leading from such a magnet to a small iron bar, which could be made to open and close as the current was turned on and off a mile away. In effect, this was a telegraph, but Henry never patented his device and it is Morse who is usually credited with the invention. Although Henry discovered the principle of induction in 1830, he again missed the credit, which went instead to Faraday. However, Henry did receive credit for discovering the *law of self-induction*, which bears his name. He published a paper in 1831 describing the electric motor—the forerunner of all such motors used today. In 1846, Henry became the first secretary of the newly established Smithsonian Institute, which became world famous under his leadership. After his death, the International Electrical Congress agreed to honor him by naming the unit of inductance the *henry*.

HOARD, James Lynn (1905–) American physical chemist, professor of chemistry at Cornell University since 1946. Hoard's research includes x-ray studies of the structure of crystals and molecules, and thermodynamic and diffusion studies of polymer solvent systems.

JOULE, James Prescott (1818–1889) English physicist, know for his researches in the mechanical equivalent of heat. These studies led to a series of experiments on the equivalence of heat and energy. The *joule*, a physical unit of work equal to ten million ergs, is named for him. Joule considered the acquisition of exact quantitative data of primary importance in scientific research. In studying the relations between electrical, mechanical, and chemical effects, he discovered the first law of thermodynamics.

KEALY, Thomas Joseph (1927–   ) American organic chemist, currently on the research staff, Central Research Department, E. I. DuPont de Nemours and Company. Kealy is noted for his work on reaction mechanisms, unstable and highly reactive structures, allene chemistry, metallocenes, and organo-sulfur compounds.

KEKULÉ von Stradonitz, Friedrich August (1829–1896) German chemist, who was the first to suggest the idea that one carbon atom can combine with four others, and that one, two, or three of the four carbon bonds can be attached to another carbon atom, thus forming "carbon-atom chains." *Kekulé structures*, as they were called, created a storm of controversy at the time. These structures, depicting the organic molecule, were made three-dimensional by Van't Hoff and Le Bel, incorporated into Lewis' electronic theory, and later elaborated by Pauling through quantum mechanics.

KENDREW, John Cowdrey (1917–   ) English biochemist, one of the team of molecular biochemists working under the direction of Max Perutz at the famous Cavendish Laboratory, Cambridge. While Perutz was working on the vastly complex structure of hemoglobin, Kendrew undertook x-ray diffraction studies of the distribution of individual atoms in myoglobin (the simpler but still enormously complicated muscular hemoglobin). In 1960, Kendrew succeeded in determining that myoglobin consists of a helical chain composed of amino acid residues. Shortly thereafter Perutz was also successful in his analysis of hemoglobin. For their unique achievements in determining the molecular structure of these key substances of the body, Kendrew and Perutz shared the 1962 Nobel prize in chemistry. (*See also* Crick; Perutz.)

LANGMUIR, Irving (1881–1957) American physical chemist, whose research work, embracing chemistry, physics, and engineering, was mainly done during his long association with the General Electric Research Laboratories. His studies of vacuum phenomena led to fundamental investigations of adsorbed films and surfaces, and the properties of electrical discharges in high vacuum and in gases at low pressures. In 1932, Langmuir received the Nobel prize in chemistry "for his discoveries and investigations in surface chemistry."

LARMOR, Sir Joseph (1857–1942) British mathematician and physicist, especially noted for his contributions to the dynamics of rotating and precessing spheres.

LAUE, Max Theodor Felix von (1879–1960) German physicist, originator of x-ray crystallography. In 1912, von Laue discovered that x rays are diffracted when passed through a crystal. This provided a convenient method of measuring x-ray wavelengths. He was assisted in his investigations by his colleagues, P. Knipping and W. Friedrich, who carried out experiments suggested by von Laue. His studies also included the theory of relativity and atomic structure. In 1914, von Laue was awarded the Nobel prize in physics "for his discovery of the diffraction of Röntgen rays in crystals."

LAUFFER, Max Augustus (1914–   ) American biophysicist, dean of the division of natural sciences, University of Pittsburgh, since 1956. Lauffer is known for his work in the biophysics of viruses and the kinetics of virus disintegration, as well as studies of the size and shape of macromolecules.

LE BEL, Joseph Achille (1847–1930) French chemist, who announced, independently and simultaneously with Van't Hoff, the theory of optical activity being related to molecular structure. (*See also* Van't Hoff.)

LENNARD-JONES, Sir John Edward (1894–1954) British scientist, noted for his contributions in the areas of both theoretical physics and theoretical chemistry. During World War II, he served as Director General of Scientific Research, Ministry of Supply. He is the author of numerous scientific papers.

LEWIS, Gilbert Newton (1875–1946) American chemist, who joined the faculty of the University of California in 1912. Lewis is noted for introducing students of chemistry to the chemical thermodynamics originally set forth by J. Willard Gibbs and for clarifying these concepts. He was the first to suggest that bonds in organic compounds are not necessarily formed through the transfer of electrons, but can form through electron sharing. He was also the first to suceed in preparing "heavy water" (1933), which was later to prove so important as a means of slowing down neutrons and making them effective in initiating a chain reaction.

Lorentz, Hendrik Antoon (1853–1928) Dutch physicist, whose work was wide in scope but primarily aimed at some consistent theory for electricity, magnetism, and light. When his "electron theory" failed to explain the negative result of the Michelson-Morley experiment, Lorentz extended his work and finally arrived at the *Lorentz transformation*, which formed the basis for the restricted theory of relativity. In 1902, Lorentz and Pieter Zeeman shared the Nobel prize in physics "for their investigations concerning the influence of magnetism upon the phenomena of radiation."

Mendeleev, Dmitri Ivanovich (1834–1907) Russian chemist. After finishing college in St. Petersburg, Mendeleev went to France and Germany for graduate studies. While there, he came under the influence of Cannizzaro's views on atomic weights. Returning to Russia, he started working out an arrangement of the 63 elements known at that time. His table differed from previous attempts in that it recognized the periodic rises and falls of valence. Mendeleev's "periodic table" of the elements was first published in 1869, and he became the first Russian scientist ever to gain widespread recognition, although many scientists, being accustomed to the chaos that had existed for so long, were very reluctant to accept the simplicity of Mendeleev's orderly arrangement. Later, in 1871, Mendeleev advanced his most important idea—leaving gaps for undiscovered elements. When increasing numbers of such elements were actually found, Mendeleev became world famous. He just missed (by one vote!) receiving the 1906 Nobel prize in chemistry. In recognition of his unique contribution, element 101 was later named in his honor.

Mössbauer, Rudolf L. (1929–) German physicist, Professor of Physics at California Institute of Technology since 1961. Mössbauer and Robert L. Hofstader of Stanford University shared the 1961 Nobel prize for separate and unrelated contributions to physics. Mössbauer was cited for his discovery of the recoilless resonance absorption of gamma rays in atomic nuclei, an effect he first observed in 1956, while carrying out an experiment in preparation for his doctoral dissertation.

MULLIKEN, Robert Sanderson (1896–) American chemist and physicist, Professor at the University of Chicago. Mulliken is known for his important work on the application of wave mechanics to molecules with the molecular orbital theory. He has also contributed significantly to the theory and nomenclature of molecular spectroscopy and the concept of electronegativity.

PAULI, Wolfgang (1900–) Theoretical physicist, born in Austria. Since 1935, Pauli has not only held the post of professor of theoretical physics at the Federal Technical High School in Zurich, but has also been a visiting professor at the Institute for Advanced Study at Princeton University, as well as at the University of Michigan and Purdue University. In 1946, Pauli became a naturalized citizen of the United States. Like Heisenberg, Pauli studied under both Arnold Sommerfeld and Max Born, and he also spent time with Niels Bohr. Unlike Heisenberg, however, he based his work on the Bohr-Sommerfeld theory. He was awarded the 1945 Nobel prize in physics "for his discovery of the exclusion principle, also called the Pauli Principle." Based originally on the old quantum theory, this principle must always be taken into account in problems of atomic structure.

PAULING, Linus Carl (1901–) American chemist, noted for having revolutionized accepted views of molecular structure by explaining the chemical bond on the basis of quantum mechanics and the theory of electrons as wave forms. Since about 1936, Pauling has devoted most of his research to biochemical problems, applying his ideas of molecular structure to molecules in living tissue, including proteins. In 1954, Pauling was awarded the Nobel prize in chemistry "for his research into the nature of the chemical bond and its application to the elucidation of the structure of complex substances." The only person besides Marie Curie to receive two Nobel prizes, he was awarded the 1963 Nobel prize in peace for his vigorous fight against nuclear testing.

PERUTZ, Max Ferdinand (1914–) Austrian-British biochemist, whose major research for the past twenty-five years has been involved with determining the structure of hemoproteins. When he first came to Cambridge University in 1936, his interest in the x-ray diffraction of proteins was stimulated by the encouraging guidance of William H. Bragg. Following World War II, Perutz organized and directed the group of molecular chemists at Cambridge who have since so distinguished themselves. While one of his group, John Kendrew, worked with myoglobin, Perutz himself concentrated on hemoglobin, whose structure is extremely complex. In 1960, shortly after Kendrew's success with myoglobin, Perutz announced his own results, having determined from x-ray diffraction studies that hemoglobin is composed of four units, each similar to the myoglobin molecule. Perutz and Kendrew shared the 1962 Nobel prize in chemistry for their singular achievements. (*See also* Kendrew; Crick.)

PLANCK, Max (1857–1947) German theoretical physicist, who made the significant discovery that energy exists in quantized form. From this premise, he derived the universal *Law of Radiation* in 1901. Professor of physics at Kiel and at Berlin, Planck was the author of such classic works on theoretical physics as *Theory of Heat Radiation*. In 1918 he was awarded the Nobel prize in physics "for his contribution to the development of physics by his discovery of the element of action."

PURCELL, Edward Mills (1912–)American physicist. Since 1938, Purcell has been on the faculty at Harvard University. Purcell published in 1946 his experimental methods (similar to Felix Bloch's) for determining the nuclear magnetic moments of substances in the solid and liquid states. He is also noted for his later work in radio astronomy. Purcell and Bloch shared the 1952 Nobel prize in physics " for their development of new methods for nuclear magnetic precision measurements and discoveries in connection therewith."

RAMAN, Sir Chandrasekhara Venkata (1888–) Indian physicist, noted for his discovery of the *Raman effect*. Most spectra due to the rotation and vibration of molecules lie in the far infrared, outside the visible range, but the Raman spectrum lies within the visible region, and has thus proved to be extremely important in studying molecular structure. Raman was awarded the 1930 Nobel prize in physics "for his work on the scattering of light and for his discovery of the effect named after him." In recognition of his achievements, the British government knighted Raman in 1929.

RAMSAY, Sir William (1852–1916) Scottish chemist, who once said that his taste for chemistry was inherited from his paternal grandfather, a chemical manufacturer, and from his maternal grandfather who was a medical man. Whatever its origin, his "taste for chemistry" bore amazingly fruitful results. He is noted for having first discovered the inert gas argon, and then continuing his researches until he had discovered other "noble gases"—neon, krypton, and xenon—enlarging the periodic system by a complete new group. He also identified the gas that results from treating certain uranium minerals with acids as being helium. The skillful methods developed by Ramsay and his associates during these investigations proved more and more important as it became necessary in radioactivity and in biochemistry to work with minute amounts of various substances. Ramsay was knighted in 1902, and was awarded the 1904 Nobel prize in chemistry "for his discovery of gaseous, indifferent elements in the air and the determination of their place in the periodic system."

RAYLEIGH, Lord (John William Strutt) (1842–1919) English physicist, who also made important contributions to chemistry. Rayleigh's first published work, dealing with electromagnetic phenomena, appeared in 1869. In the next ten years, his researches embraced nearly every branch of physics. In 1879, he succeeded James Clerk Maxwell as director of the world-famous Cavendish Laboratory at Cambridge University, serving with singular distinction until his resignation in 1884. One of his important investigations concerned the accurate determination of the *ohm*, the practical unit of electrical resistance. Rayleigh was awarded the 1904 Nobel prize in physics "for his work on the density of gases and his discovery, in this connection, of argon."

ROBERTSON, John Monteath (1900–   ) Scottish chemist. Robertson served as Scientific Advisor to the Ministry of Aircraft Production during World War II, and has held the honorary post since that time. In 1942, he became Gardiner Professor of Chemistry at the University of Glasgow. He is the author of numerous scientific papers, mainly on chemical subjects.

RUTHERFORD, Ernest (1871–1937) British physicist, born in New Zealand. Rutherford was the first to discover the components of radioactive emission (called alpha, beta, and gamma rays). From his study of alpha rays, he derived the first successful model of the atom in 1912, and discovered the disintegration of nuclei by bombardment with alpha particles. He was awarded the Nobel prize in chemistry in 1908 "for his investigation into the disintegration of the elements and the chemistry of radioactive substances."

SANGER, Frederick (1918–) English biochemist, whose distinguished work in determining the precise structure of the amino acid chain of protein molecules has been carried on at Cambridge University's famous Cavendish Laboratory. In 1953, after eight years of concentrated effort, he succeeded in working out the exact order of the amino acids in the insulin molecule. This significant breakthrough opened the way for the work of other chemists, including Sanger's colleagues Perutz and Kendrew. Sanger was awarded the 1958 Nobel prize in chemistry "for his work on the structure of proteins, especially insulin." (*See also* Perutz; Kendrew; Crick.)

SCHRÖDINGER, Erwin (1887–) German physicist, noted for having introduced wave mechanics, an advanced form of quantum theory, which made it possible to compute parameters and physical characteristics of the atom. He shared the Nobel prize in physics with Paul Dirac in 1933 "for the discovery of new and fruitful forms of atomic theory."

SELIG, Henry (1927–) German-American inorganic chemist. Since 1953, Selig has been an associate chemist at Argonne National Laboratory, working in the field of fluoride chemistry of transition metal fluorides.

THOMSON, Sir Joseph John (1856–1940) British physicist who determined the ratio of mass and charge of the electron by the deflection of cathode rays in combined electric and magnetic fields. He was awarded the 1906 Nobel prize in physics "for his theoretical and experimental investigations into the transmission of electricity through gases."

TSUTSUI, Minoru (1918–   ) Japanese-American organic chemist, currently with the Research Division of New York University. Tsutsui is noted for his work in the chemistry of terpenes, and his investigation of organometallic compounds, especially pi-complexes of metals.

VAN DER WAALS, Johannes Diderick (1837–1923) Dutch physicist, whose Ph.D. dissertation "on the continuity of the gaseous and liquid states" attracted widespread attention in 1873. His later scientific work was dominated by his main theme: a substance passes from the gaseous to the liquid state without any essential change, although its physical properties may differ in the two states. Van der Waals was awarded the 1910 Nobel prize in physics "for his work concerning the equation of state of gases and liquids."

VAN'T HOFF, Jacobus Henricus (1852–1911) Dutch physical chemist, noted for a paper he published when he was only twenty-two, explaining his theory of why some organic compounds were optically active while others were not. This introduced the then-new idea of three-dimensional tetrahedral bonding in the carbon atom, the resulting asymmetric arrangement accounting for the optical activity. Le Bel, who was also very young at the time, arrived at a similar theory independently, and the two usually share the credit. Although later Linus Pauling introduced a more sophisticated view of chemical bonds, Van't Hoff's theory is still very useful as a simple explanation of optical activity. In 1901, Van't Hoff became the first recipient of the Nobel prize in chemistry "for his discovery of laws of chemical dynamics and of osmotic pressure."

WAAGE, Peter (1833–1900) Norwegian chemist, who owed his sole claim to fame to his work with Guldberg on the *law of mass action*. (*See* Guldberg.)

WALDEN, Paul (1863–1957) Russian-born German chemist, noted for the process called *Walden inversion,* used not only for studying the end products of chemical reactions but also for investigating the intermediate steps in obtaining those products. This technique has proved to be an important tool in organic chemistry.

WASSERMAN, Edel (1932–) American theoretical and organic chemist, member of the technical staff of Bell Telephone Laboratories since 1957. Wasserman has become known for his physical, organic, and theoretical studies of the electronic structure of organic molecules. His investigations also include optical activity and large carbocyclic molecules.

WATSON, James Dewey (1928–) American biochemist, especially noted for the Watson-Crick model of DNA structure, which he and Crick developed at Cambridge University. This model was based on the physical data supplied by Wilkins and the chemical data of Chargaff. Watson, who has been on the faculty of Harvard University since 1955, shared with Crick and Wilkins the 1962 Nobel prize in medicine and physiology.

WOODWARD, Robert Burns (1917–) American chemist, who has remained at Harvard University since joining the faculty in 1938 at the age of twenty-one. In 1944, working with William von Eggers Doering, Woodward succeeded in totally synthesizing quinine. This was the first of his many outstanding achievements in organic chemistry. In the next ten years, Woodward performed remarkable feats, synthesizing cortisone, cholesterol, strychnine, and the first of the tranquilizing drugs, reserpine. The synthesis of chlorophyll followed in 1960, and two years later, a group that he headed succeeded in synthesizing a tetracycline antibiotic. Woodward's amazing skill in finding the key to nonpolymeric molecules has left few serious challenges for the organic chemist. In 1965, he was awarded the Nobel prize in chemistry.

ZEISS, Harold Hicks (1917–) American organic chemist. Zeiss has worked primarily on stereochemical problems, mechanisms of organic oxidation reactions, the structural elucidation and synthesis of naturally occurring terpenes, and various aspects of organometallic chemistry.

The Authors

Daniel Berg joined the Westinghouse Research Laboratories as a Research Physical Chemist immediately after receiving his Ph.D. from Yale University in 1953. He is now Manager of Inorganic Materials-Science and Technology.

A native New Yorker, he attended Stuyvesant High School and completed his undergraduate studies at the City College of New York, before going on to Yale. He says that as far as he remembers, he became interested in science in the first grade, if not before. "I had a chemistry laboratory in my room at home. Why? I found it fascinating—and I still do! In high school, I was very fortunate in having excellent teachers who took a *professional* interest in my scientific career, as well as in my studies."

Although his scientific work occupies a great deal of his time, Dr. Berg has many other interests, including his family—the Bergs have two children, a small son and a smaller daughter. He is a voracious reader, and is the enthusiastic leader of a Great Books Discussion Group. He also enjoys golf, fly-fishing, painting, and organ playing "in increasingly amateurish order." He adds, "And I play 95 golf!"

But Dr. Berg's status is highly professional when it comes to his numerous scientific articles. In the past few years he has also contributed chapters to a number of technical books, and acted as Editor of *Digest of Dielectrics*, published in 1963.

Robert Charles has been a staff member of the Westinghouse Research Laboratories since 1952. He is now a Fellow Chemist in the Physical Chemistry Department, primarily concerned with coordination chemistry and the chemistry of metal chelate compounds. He has published more than fifty scientific papers in these areas. At present, his particular interest is in the preparation and characterization of rare-earth chelates for use in liquid laser devices.

Born and brought up in Pittsburgh, Pennsylvania, he attended the local public schools, and then started his undergraduate work at the University of Pittsburgh, intending to become an electrical engineer. He found that one of the requirements for his chosen major was a course in chemistry. At the end of his freshman year, he was one of many students throughout the country who took a national examination in chemistry. He scored so high on this exam that his professors suggested that he ought to switch his major to chemistry. He now says that it was not too hard to go along with this unexpected change in his plans, because he had already begun to "have some doubts about being an electrical engineer."

In 1948, with a B.S. degree and Highest Honors from the University of Pittsburgh, he decided to continue his studies there as a graduate student. Four years later, he received his Ph.D. in chemistry.

Dr. Charles is unmarried and this leaves him free to devote as much time as he chooses to the enjoyment of his favorite pastimes: reading, music, and sports.

LAWRENCE EPSTEIN has been a staff member of the Westinghouse Research Laboratories since 1956. He is currently engaged in the chemical study of radiation effects on a wide variety of materials.

Born and brought up in Brooklyn, New York, he attended Townsend Harris High School, a prep school for selected students destined to study at the City College of New York. After only one term at that college, however, he transferred to Cooper Union and received his B.S. in chemical engineering in 1943. After a brief period in industry, he spent the next three years as an electronics technician in the U.S. Navy.

Once more a civilian, he went back to chemical industry for a short time. Anxious, however, to learn more of the fundamentals of science than were required in engineering practice, he began an eight-year stint of living a "triple life." Not only was he husband and father, but a full-time teacher at New York City Community College, as well as a graduate student at Brooklyn Polytechnic Institute. In 1955, he received his Ph.D., accepted a position at Mellon Institute to study synthetic rubber, and moved his family to Pittsburgh, Pennsylvania. The Epstein's fourth child had just been born at this time. He left Mellon Institute to join Westinghouse Research, where he could combine his two major interests—radiation chemistry and polymer chemistry.

Dr. Epstein says that he didn't actually "choose" a scientific career, but was "persuaded" by his family, during the economic stress of the 1930's, that it was more practical to become a chemical engineer than to pursue his interest in classical languages and music. These have now become his hobbies, and he is again teaching—evening courses in general chemistry at the University of Pittsburgh.

MILTON GOTTLIEB has been with the Westinghouse Research Laboratories since 1959, where his research work has included thermionic energy conversion and plasma physics. He is now Senior Research Physicist, working in cryophysics.

Born in New York City, Dr. Gottlieb is a product of the city's public school system. At Brooklyn Technical High School, he decided early in his physics course that he wanted to devote most of his time to science. He has never regretted this decision. He says, "As an undergraduate at the City College of New York, my interest was sharpened by my association with a great many like-minded students, whose zeal and abilities were inspiring." After receiving his B.S. degree in 1954, he continued his studies at the University of Pennsylvania, where he received his Ph.D. in physics. It was at the university that he first came in contact with people engaged in research, and learned from personal experience its excitement and its frustrations. Becoming interested in solid state physics, he chose as the subject of his doctoral thesis the absorption of optical radiation by alkali halide crystals.

The girl who became his wife he met at college, having been assigned the place next to her in a biology laboratory. He now says, "She was so remarkably proficient in the subject and I was so appallingly incompetent that a close association was inevitable." The Gottliebs have a small son who is as enthusiastic as his parents about weekend camping trips. They are hoping he may share their other enthusiasms, and perhaps prove to be a budding scientist.

Lyon Mandelcorn joined the Westinghouse Research Laboratories in 1954 as a Research Engineer. He now holds the position of Fellow Scientist. His work has included the investigation of clathrates and the properties of insulation, and at present he is concerned with the electrochemistry of anodic oxide films. He is the editor of a recently published book, *Non-Stoichiometric Compounds*.

He was born and brought up in Montreal, Canada. As a student at Baron Byng High School, he became fascinated by the idea that textbook material could be "brought to life" in laboratory experiments. This was the beginning of his interest in chemistry. After two years at Yeshiva University in New York City, he completed his chemistry major at New York University. Following his graduation in 1947, he returned to Canada for graduate studies at McGill University, and in 1951 received his Ph.D. in physical chemistry. Granted a Post Doctoral Fellowship, he spent the next two years at the National Research Council of Canada, working in the area of photochemistry.

Dr. Mandelcorn, who spends a good deal of his spare time on Hebrew religious studies, Biblical and Talmudical, enjoys his active role in the affairs of Hillel Academy of Pittsburgh, a Hebrew Day School. The Mandelcorns have two sons, four and nine years old, and an eight-year-old daughter. He says, "Much of my life is centered around my family and, in a sense, I am growing up again with my children."

JAMES MCHUGH came to the Westinghouse Research Laboratories in 1957 as a Research Chemist. Now a Senior Scientist, he is primarily engaged in various areas of solid state chemistry.

Born in Pittsburgh, Pennsylvania, he received his early education in the local public schools. He recalls that his interest in science, particularly chemistry, dates back to his grade school days. By the time he was a high school senior, this interest had developed into an ambition to prepare himself for a scientific career. Although he found the offer of a music scholarship tempting, he declined it in favor of studying chemistry at Duquesne University. In 1953, he graduated summa cum laude with a B.S. degree in chemistry. During this time, his summers had been occupied working as a caddy, and later as a clerk for the Isaly Dairy Company. As a college undergraduate, he was employed part-time in the Research Laboratories of Jones and Laughlin Steel Corporation.

Awarded a National Science Foundation Fellowship, he went on for graduate studies at California Institute of Technology, and the following year he became a Graduate Teaching Assistant. He chose molecular structure as the subject of his doctoral thesis, and in 1957 he received his Ph.D. in physical chemistry.

The McHughs have four young children who occupy a good deal of their attention, but they still find time for their two avid interests—reading and numismatics. At present, they are making an enjoyable hobby of accumulating a library of outstanding nonfiction books, with particular emphasis on history and art.

ARMAND PANSON joined the Westinghouse Research Laboratories in 1956 as a Research Chemist. He now holds the position of Fellow Scientist, and has recently been investigating the use of x-ray absorption edge spectroscopy as a tool for solid state chemical research. He is particularly interested in understanding electrical conduction mechanisms in solids.

A native New Englander, he was born in Fall River, Massachusetts, and brought up in Providence, Rhode Island. He became interested in chemistry at an early age and decided to pursue this interest with a view to a scientific career. After completing his undergraduate studies at Brown University in Providence, he went on to the University of Pennsylvania in Philadelphia for graduate work. In 1957, he received his Ph.D. in physical chemistry.

Dr. Panson and his wife find that their year-old son is not too young to share their enthusiasm for hiking trips. This hobby has led to Dr. Panson's active participation in the American Youth Hostels. Hiking during the summer months keeps the Pansons in condition for skiing in the winter, and they are now planning to put their son on skiis by the time he is two.

For Further Reading

PART ONE

Basolo, Fred, and Pearson, Ralph G. *Mechanisms of Inorganic Reactions.* New York: John Wiley & Sons, 1958.

Cotton, Frank A., and Wilkinson, Geoffrey. *Advanced Inorganic Chemistry.* New York: Interscience Publishers, 1962.

Coulson, Charles Alfred. *Valence.* 2nd ed. New York: Oxford University Press, 1961.

Dekker, Adrianus J. *Solid State Physics.* Englewood Cliffs, N.J.: Prentice-Hall, 1957.

Eyring, Henry, and Eyring, Edward M. *Modern Chemical Kinetics.* New York: Reinhold Publishing Corp., 1963.

Glasstone, Samuel. *Textbook of Physical Chemistry.* 2nd ed. Princeton, N.J.: D. Van Nostrand Co., 1946. Note: Chapter I, "Atomic Structure and Atomic Spectra"; Chapter V, "The Solid State."

Gould, Edwin S. *Mechanism and Structure in Organic Chemistry.* New York: Holt, Rinehart and Winston, 1959.

Hinshelwood, Cyril Norman. *The Structure of Physical Chemistry.* Oxford: Clarendon Press, 1951.

Pauling, Linus. *The Nature of the Chemical Bond.* 3rd ed. Ithaca, N.Y.: Cornell University Press, 1960.

Pauling, Linus, and Wilson, E. Bright, Jr. *Introduction to Quantum Mechanics.* New York: McGraw-Hill Book Co., 1935.

PART TWO

Allen, John M., editor. *The Molecular Control of Cellular Activity.* New York: McGraw-Hill Book Co., 1962.

Bailar, J. C., editor. *The Chemistry of Coordination Compounds.* New York: Reinhold Publishing Corp., 1956.

Bartlett, N., "Noble Gas Compounds," *International Science & Technology* (September 1964) p. 56.

Bohn, R. K., Katada, K., Martinez, J. V., and Bauer, S. H. *Noble Gas Compounds.* Chicago: University of Chicago Press, 1963.

Chernick, C. L., "Chemical Compounds of the Noble Gases," *Record of Chemical Progress 24* (1963), p. 139.

Dwyer, F. P., and Mellor, D. P., editors. *Chelating Agents and Metal Chelates.* New York: Academic Press, 1964.

Edsall, John Tileston, and Wyman, Jeffries. *Biophysical Chemistry.* New York: Academic Press, 1958.

Fischer, E. O., and Fritz, H. P., " Compounds of Aromatic Ring Systems and Metals," *Advances in Inorganic Chemistry & Radiochemistry 1*, p. 55–115. H. J. Emeleus and A. G. Sharpe, editors, Academic Press, New York, 1959.

Frisch, H. L., and Wasserman, E. "Chemical Topology," *Journal of the American Chemical Society 83* (1961), p. 3789.

Glasstone, Samuel. *Textbook of Theoretical Chemistry.* Princeton, N.J.: D. Van Nostrand Company, 1944.

Hildebrand, J. H., and Scott, R. L. *The Solubility of Nonelectrolytes.* A.C.S. Monograph Series. New York: Reinhold Publishing Corp., 1950.

Holloway, J. H., "Reactions of the Noble Gases," *Progress in Inorganic Chemistry 6*, p. 241–269, F.A. Cotton, editor, New York: Interscience, 1964.

Jones, M. M. *Elementary Coordination Chemistry.* Englewood Cliffs, N.J.: Prentice-Hall, 1964.

Klotz, Irving Myron. *Energetics in Biochemical Reactions.* New York: Academic Press, 1957.

Kornberg, Arthur. *Biosynthesis of DNA.* University Park, Pa.: The Pennsylvania State University Press, 1964.

Krebs, H. A., Kornberg, H. L., and Burton K. *Energy Transformations in Living Matter.* Berlin: Springer-Verlag, 1957.

Lemberg, R., and Legge, J. W. *Hematin Compounds and Bile Pigments*. New York: Interscience Publishers, 1949.

Mandelcorn, Lyon, editor. *Non-Stoichiometric Compounds*. New York: Academic Press, 1964.

Martell, A. E., and Calvin, M. *Chemistry of the Metal Chelate Compounds*. Englewood Cliffs, N.J.: Prentice-Hall, 1956.

Martin, D. F., and Martin B. B. *Coordination Compounds*. New York: McGraw-Hill Book Co., 1964.

Neilands, J. B., and Stumpf, Paul K. *Enzyme Chemistry*. New York: John Wiley & Sons, 1958.

Pimentel, George C. *The Hydrogen Bond*. New York: Reinhold Publishing Corp., 1960.

Setlow, Richard B., and Pollard, Ernest C. *Molecular Biophysics*. Reading, Mass.: Addison-Wesley Publishing Co., 1962.

Wasserman, E., "The Preparation of Interlocking Rings," *Journal of the American Chemical Society 82* (1960), p. 4433.

Wilkinson, G. A., and Cotton, F. A., "Cyclopentadienyl and Arene Metal Compounds," *Progress in Inorganic Chemistry 1*, p. 1–126, F. A. Cotton, editor, New York: Interscience, 1959.

PART THREE

Bragg, William H., and Bragg, William L. *X-Rays and Crystal Structure*. 4th ed. London: G. Bell & Sons, 1924.

Brügel, Werner. *An Introduction to Infrared Spectroscopy*. Translated from the German. New York: John Wiley & Sons, 1962.

Clark, George L., editor. *The Encyclopedia of Spectroscopy*. New York: Reinhold Publishing Corp., 1960.

Gordy, Walter, Smith, William V., and Trambarulo, Ralph F. *Microwave Spectroscopy*. New York: John Wiley & Sons, 1953.

McLachlan, Dan. *X-Ray Crystal Structure*. New York: McGraw-Hill Book Co., 1957.

Szymanski, Herman A. *Theory & Practice of Infrared Spectroscopy*. New York: Plenum Press. 1964.

Wertheim, Gunther K. *Mössbauer Effect: Principles and Application*. New York: Academic Press, 1964.

Index

Numbers in italic refer to figures and photographs.